Living with Dementia - A Son's Story

By

Robin Spice

British Library Cataloguing In Publication Data
A Record of this Publication is available
from the British Library

ISBN 1846854482
978-1-84685-448-4

First Published 2007 by

Exposure Publishing, an imprint of Diggory Press,
Three Rivers, Minions, Liskeard, Cornwall, PL14 5LE, UK
WWW.DIGGORYPRESS.COM

Contents

Acknowledgements

This account has been difficult to write for a variety of reasons. The discipline required and finding the time being just two. Also, in the months following the events described in this book, some of the detail was just too painful to have to think about which meant my progress was slow. After I started I was full of doubts - doubts about how much I would be able to write, how much detail to include, whether I would ever finish it and finally, if I did, how it would be received by those closest to the story and others whose opinions I value.

All these doubts were eventually lifted by the support and encouragement of a number of people and I should like to acknowledge them here. There is my brother Howard, who bravely rose to the challenge of reading the first draft when I am sure he would have preferred not to; my cousin David Tudor for his valuable input in a number of ways; David Pennant, who as an author himself provided some useful information and constructive comments, and last but not least, Monica Carly, who gamely offered to utilise her editorial skills on this work, not knowing at the time what she was letting herself in for! I am also indebted to Monica for the additional assistance she gave me to ensure this account made sense. A word of thanks to Lindy Banks and Nick Roach because, without their intervention, the book you are now holding would not have been published in the form it is. Finally, to my family, and in particular my wife Maggie, for her constant love and support throughout.

All royalties/proceeds from the sale of this book will be donated to the Alzheimer's Society to aid the important work they undertake in raising awareness and supporting sufferers of all types of dementia and their families/carers.

Introduction

"We come together to give thanks for 77 years in the life of Julia Dorothy Spice. We give thanks for Julie, for Mum, for Nanny, for a Sister, an Aunt. We come to mourn her death. I think she wouldn't want us to – but that's how it is because for some of us she has quite simply always been there. Always.

Julie joined the choir here at St Mary's and remained for the best part of 30 years. This was a significant part of her life, a significant part of her daily routine, her weekly routine. She loved it. Working, to get those alto notes just right, practising at home all hours.

Julie was industrious and this industry can be seen in the number of jobs she took on to make sure the ends would meet. She was independent. She was resilient. 20 years ago, breast cancer was diagnosed. She underwent a mastectomy. She coped. She thrived. She survived. Health was important to her; she was forever reading books to do with health issues and went to exercise classes with the Women's League of Health and Beauty.

In the thirty-one years I have been in England, Julie was my honorary Mother. Putting me up, feeding me while I revised for my exams and my finals. Being there at my Graduations; being there at my Ordinations and at my Wedding. Always there. Immaculate, radiant, smiling, loving.

After being diagnosed with dementia, Julie moved to a warden assisted establishment and later into residential care. In June 2005 she was admitted to hospital where she died on 24 August with her sons watching her safely from this life to the next.

When we say that she died, it sounds as though something ended. But not for her. The only thing that ended was her pain. On 24 August, she became free. That cloud of confusion was lifted. And she became more herself than she has been for some time. And that is what we give thanks for – she is gone, not dead. Gone to the God who created her, whom she served so well for her whole life and particularly in singing praise to Him in this place of worship. Gone, by the grace of God – reunited with one whom she has loved longest and missed most!"

(Taken from the eulogy at Julie's funeral given by her cousin, Revd David St C Tudor)

Foreword

Mum grabbed a set of keys from the table and hurled them at me. What deep sense of frustration and anxiety that led to such an uncharacteristic act can only be surmised. She was in such distress she could find no other way of dealing with her feelings. If this action was a sign that she had realised she was losing control of her mental faculties, and as a result, of her life, it must have been a terrible cross to carry.

For me, watching my mother in such anguish, was unbearable. So many different emotions flooded through me. Here I was trying to do my utmost to make life a little easier for her – since it was obviously not safe for her to go on living in her house – only to find she was desperately unhappy. A warden assisted flat had seemed the right answer but Mum was not accepting of the situation hence the throwing of keys incident the day after she had moved in. She did not know why she was there, it was all my doing and she wanted to go 'home'.

Foremost in my mind was sorrow that life was, and would continue to be, so hard for her now and the helplessness I felt because all I wanted to do was make things better for her. Then there was the humiliation of all this upset happening in the presence of the warden and the overall feeling of my being, at that point, desperately alone.

Of course there was my brother and my family but the responsibility weighed heavily on me as the elder son. Certainly in those early days the road ahead was unclear and I often did not know which path to take but I always hoped I was doing the right thing when quite often it was never clear what the right thing might be. Looking back it is easy now to

9

recognise the many mistakes made due to my lack of understanding about what was happening and how I should deal with it.

I cannot have been the first person to find coping with a loved one who is suffering from dementia so difficult – and I am sure I will not be the last – but at the time, when it was all happening, I had so little guidance.

This has made me feel that if I had known how someone else had faced it and just what the issues involved would be, at least I would have felt a little more confident and perhaps have been a more effective carer. For this reason, when it was all over, I resolved to set everything down in writing, in the hope that perhaps my story might bring some comfort to others who find themselves in a similar situation.

Here, then, is my story – or rather – that of my mother – in all its painful details, in memory of the mother whose two sons loved her so devotedly.

Prologue

My mother, Julie Spice, passed away in August 2005 at Epsom General Hospital. I find it difficult to use the word "died". It seems much more brutal a word and to the point. "Passed away" is a gentler description and in fact more accurate of how it was when the time came.

Julie was the wife of Don and the mother of two sons – Robin (that's me, the elder son) and Howard. My father was much older than my mother and quite strict. He did not have much to do with our upbringing on a day to day basis, as he used to readily admit, so if anybody thought that he might not be that close to us, particularly when we were growing up, they would be right, with the result that both my brother and I were closer to my mother. She was everything one could wish a mother to be: kind, loyal, generous, loving, warm, thoughtful and devoted in every way to all of her family. She was also a very genuine person, quick to compliment when she thought it was deserved but equally, careful to remain silent if she felt the reverse was the case. Of course she was not perfect – who is? Her biggest fault was allowing people to take advantage of her. However, whether this was by her husband, her sons, or other people, she never complained, probably because she just did not see it like that. While in many ways I loved her for being like this, I often felt some injustice, that as a result of invariably putting other people first, her interests always seemed to take second place or were lost altogether. I suppose I am saying I felt she had a bit of a raw deal and that as a result she did not get the recognition in life that she deserved – recognition in terms of being fully appreciated for what she gave throughout her life. She was definitely one of life's givers, not a taker, and a person who accepted her lot without complaint.

As a result of Dad being much older, my mother was left a widow for fifteen years. It is probably true to say that she never really recovered from his death. Of course she had the full support of her family at the time and on a continuing basis but I don't think the shock of losing him really ever left her, such was the love she had for him.

What follows is not just an account of what happened to my mother when she developed dementia. I would like this narrative to be viewed as a tribute to my mother for a life which at first glance might be considered unremarkable but on closer reading perhaps demands some respect and even admiration.

EARLY DAYS

Julia Dorothy Harrison was born in St Margaret's, Twickenham in 1927 on Guy Fawkes Day to Dorothy and Percival Harrison. Percival was a managing clerk at a firm of solicitors in Bedford Row, London, and prior to their marriage in 1924 Dorothy was a cashier in a butcher's shop but, as was the case in those days, she gave up work completely after their marriage.

Although baptised Julia after her mother's grandmother, from a baby she was always known as Julie. It is not clear how this came about but the name Julie certainly stuck. Most of my mother's birthday cards which she received on her first birthday read "to Julie". Julie was blessed with curly copper-coloured hair but not the freckles which many red-headed people tend to possess. Early photographs of her as a young woman clearly show that this curly mane was difficult to control, but it was nonetheless very striking, and at that time, particularly, must have made her stand out from the crowd. The family became complete in 1932 when Julie's brother, Kenneth, was born. He also had red hair, but perhaps luckily for him, no curls.

Home was a three-bedroomed terraced property, an early 1900s house, typical of the London suburbs. It was probably quite a pleasant road at one time but these days, like many other areas, it has become choked with parked cars. Dorothy lived there until her death in 1987 when the house passed to Julie's brother who did not finally leave until 1998. Since then the house has been completely modernised with walls knocked down, and other internal changes. It is now, like other similar properties, worth over £400,000. Julie's parents would be staggered if they knew but equally aghast, I am sure, at what has been done to their beloved house where Dorothy had lived for fifty-eight years.

Percival died on Christmas Eve 1966 from coronary thrombosis at the age of seventy-four and Dorothy was left a widow for what turned out to be twenty-one years. She could be a difficult woman, seeming to be happier when she had something to complain about than something to smile about. Like all of us, her personality was shaped by her early life, when it is probably true to say she was overshadowed by her younger sister and brother. The death of Dorothy's elder brother at the age of three may also have had some bearing on how she was treated by her parents, albeit unintentionally. As a consequence she developed a "chip on the shoulder" which unfortunately it seemed she was unable to overcome. Yet she could be generous at times and could smile and even laugh when she wanted to. In fact at these times her appearance and demeanour seemed to change so completely that she might just as well have been a different person. I did not know Percival well but I can recall that he was a bit of a joker and enjoyed a laugh whereas for much of the time Dorothy was serious and prone to telling Percival off and often nagging about something or other. I recall my father perhaps unkindly saying that it was this nagging that led to his death.

My mother had an average education with maths being her best subject. At sixteen she took lessons in typewriting and passed the relevant Pitman's examination of the time with flying colours. Brownies and Guides played an important part in her life as did a strong association with the local church. Julie's mother was a Mother's Union stalwart and her dad, a churchwarden. In the First World War he suffered badly in the trenches and as a result of frostbite had at least one toe amputated. In the Second World War he was an air raid warden.

Mum's first job after leaving school was that of a dental secretary at a dentist's practice. This probably explains why she always noticed people's teeth. It is fair to say this was something she probably observed first on meeting new people and often commented on before anything else! It may also explain her later dedication to ensuring that my brother and I both had our teeth straightened. During the late 60s, and early 70s we made numerous visits to a Brighton orthodontist (where we were living at the time) and then when we moved to Surrey, visited the same one every six weeks even though his surgery was in Harley Street, London!

Music was always a feature of my mother's life and she learned to play the piano and reached Grade Seven in pianoforte examinations. Mum was a competent pianist and in later life inherited the piano which has been in the family since the 1920s. This piano is now mine but I am told by the piano tuner that, not surprisingly, it is on its last legs!

Singing was also another attribute she possessed as did her father and brother who sang in church choirs both locally and at Southwark Cathedral in London. From 1973 my mother sang in the church choir at the village church in Horsell, Woking. She started as a soprano but soon became an alto at a time when the choir was short of ladies to sing this part. For a while both my brother and I were also in the choir at the same time as she was but due to his voice breaking my brother left in 1975, and I eventually left in 1981. However, my mother's membership of the choir continued until early 2003 when her illness took hold.

15

Julie with Don on holiday in 1950

I believe it was about 1949 that my mother met my father Donald. By that time my mother was working for the National Rail company and was based at London Bridge. My father used to tell the story of how he first became aware of her through hearing her laugh in the office next to his. The black and white photographs taken at this time show a happy couple. My mother would have been twenty-three but my father was considerably older, although he did not look it. Throughout his whole life he did not look his age, but he was born in 1913 which meant that he was fourteen years older than Mum, making him thirty-seven when they first met.

From what I can gather my mother had had a serious relationship prior to my father. Harry was his name and he was a musician who eventually became the organist at Llandaff Cathedral in Wales. It is not clear exactly why the relationship did not work out although it is probable the distance between them after Harry moved out of the area did not help. The relationship my mother and father had was obviously the real thing and I say this particularly because of the circumstances which were never made known to my brother or me until 1990, after my father passed away.

My father had been married before. His first wife's name was Sybil and she was a Roman Catholic. I have no idea when the relationship with Sybil foundered but believe that this happened prior to his meeting Mum, although I cannot be certain because of the absolute secrecy surrounding the whole matter. As Sybil was a Roman Catholic she would not agree to a divorce, so when my mother met Dad he was still a married man. It is a reflection of the love they obviously had for one another that they decided not to let this fact stand in their way because they eventually set up home together in a caravan on a site in the village of Pembury, near Tonbridge, in Kent.

This could not have been an easy decision to make, particularly in view of Julie's mother who must have been far from pleased, steeped as she was in the life of her local church and Mothers Union. It is interesting to note that in fact Julie's great-grandmother also had children out of wedlock, but whether Julie's mother knew this and was therefore more tolerant than she would otherwise have been of Julie's situation we will never know. It is possible that this stigma, as it would have been viewed at that time, was borne silently so that later generations remained unaware. Certainly, in the early 1950s, never mind the 1800s, co-habiting was far from the norm, so very different were those times from today.

So it was in these circumstances that I was born in December 1954 and my brother in October 1959, by which time we were living in Richmond. From then up until July 1990 we remained in complete ignorance of the fact that our parents were not married, or rather remained unmarried until the 1970s. Mum had changed her name by deed poll very early on so she could be known as Mrs Spice and we understood finally, and perhaps not surprisingly, that it was Dad who didn't want us to know for whatever reason, and, of course, in our house Dad almost always had the final say.

Neither of us will ever forget the moment when Mum told us. It was shortly after Dad had passed away and the vicar was visiting to discuss the funeral arrangements. Without any warning whatsoever Mum told us of Dad's previous marital status and that they were not married until many years later. We were both stunned. It was one of the few times I can say that I felt as if I had been kicked in the stomach – such was the effect this news had on me. It was a shock because apart from anything else, we could not imagine our parents being different from any others. Indeed, 'conventional' is the word which could be used to describe them, and here we were being told that in fact they had acted totally unconventionally by living together and having two children.

Mum was insistent that it made no difference to anything, that we were loved just as much and treated no differently, and, of course, she was right. Still, it seemed an unbelievable secret to keep from us, their sons, all that time, particularly as they did eventually marry in 1977. Did it make any difference to us that they were not married for so long? No, not at all, but would it have done had we known? Again no, but personally I regret the fact that my father had not felt able to tell us when we were adults and given us the opportunity to fully understand their situation and the actions they took as a result. If he had been a younger man it might have made a difference, but he was forty-two years old when I was born and the age/generation gap was perhaps too great for him to act or think differently.

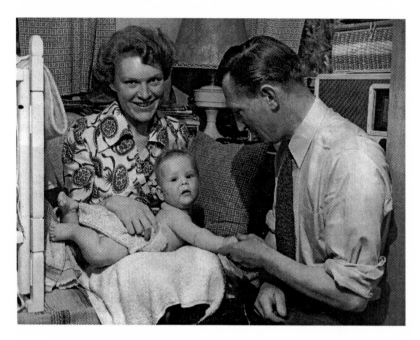

Me with Mum & Dad in the caravan 1955

What prompted them to finally tie the knot is unclear but it might have been to do with the fact that by 1977 my wife and I had met and our relationship was serious although there was no suggestion of marriage until a year later. However, it may have started them thinking about marriage themselves and so prompted Dad eventually to ask Sybil for a divorce to which she agreed. I recently obtained a copy of the marriage certificate and it confirms that Mum and Dad married at Woking Registry Office on 5 January 1977 with my Dad's brother and his wife acting as witnesses, presumably two of the very few people who were in the know.

It must have been difficult for my parents because on more than one occasion in my teens I do recall broaching the subject by asking why there were no wedding photographs on display. Julie's mother had photos of other family weddings but none of Mum and Dad's. I was fobbed off with the fact that theirs was a registry office wedding and no photographs were taken. My mother also, as I now know, made up a date of their wedding, 15 June, with the result that for several years I would produce a wedding anniversary card for them. Little did I know how much more difficult I must have made things, particularly for Mum, who was having to comply with Dad's request for us not to be told the truth.

As far as the wider family were concerned it did not appear to make any difference to them either. We regularly visited my father's clan in Kent including our paternal grandparents. Although I was well aware that my father and my maternal grandmother did not always see eye to eye I don't believe this was anything to do with Mum and Dad's marital status. It was more a personality and strength of character clash. That our relationship with our maternal grandparents was not in any way affected was confirmed to me when I recently came across birthday cards my brother and I received as babies from the age of one onwards. Neither Dorothy nor Percival may have liked the situation but they were not going to let it prevent them from enjoying a normal relationship with their grandchildren.

In 1983 Mum was diagnosed with breast cancer. We were devastated, not least because my wife and I were expecting our first child. She bore the news and its aftermath stoically to the extent that, looking back, I think it was a case of Mum supporting us rather than us supporting her. I really believed it was the beginning of the end, but very fortunately it had been caught early. A mastectomy was required but no other treatment. Mum had annual check-ups for the following 12 years and at each one she received the all clear.

Conversely, my father's death in July 1990 was to have a profound effect on her.

Mum had been working as a night supervisor at an approved school in Ottershaw since the 1960s. At the start she worked two or three nights a week but over time these gradually reduced to one. So it was, that this particular evening she was at work and on returning home the following morning found my father collapsed in the bathroom. He was taken to hospital where he suffered another major stroke that left him unconscious. I was in New York at the time on a two week business trip so had to return early. Dad subsequently passed away five days later, on his 77th birthday. At first Mum seemed okay and appeared to be coping but it soon became obvious that all was not well and later she was diagnosed as suffering from clinical depression. As observed by my cousin David, her reaction to his death and her life in the months which followed is reflected exactly in the words of the following poem:

When we were married they told us we were one
But they never told us what to do
When half of one has gone.
What do you do with half a life
Or half a will to care,
What do you do with half a heart
Now the other half's not there?
You were the other half of me
A heart linked to my own.
What do I do with half a life
Now I am on my own?

The depression lasted for two years during which time she spent a lot of money and accumulated debts amounting to £20,000. She became somewhat aggressive at times, her behaviour and demeanour often manic. She did not take kindly to being advised or helped and to all intents and purposes she changed in character completely from her usual easy-going nature. With help from us, her GP, and others, she eventually overcame this trauma but coping with this situation left its mark on all of us.

Once Mum's recovery was complete we had to deal with the debts. Mum didn't want to move house at that time and she was no longer earning, having had to retire from the school. I therefore decided that the best way forward would be for me to take out a loan consolidating her debts and she could repay me, as and when. When both my wife Maggie and I decided to work full-time, we needed somebody to take care of the children after school. Mum needed something to do to keep her occupied and so it was that we agreed to a business arrangement. We would pay her to take care of the children every day and she would repay the loan by us deducting a monthly amount from these earnings. It worked very well for all concerned and I believe also gave Mum back a sense of being needed and having a purpose in life which she had substantially lost when Dad passed away.

Mum eventually moved to a smaller property in 1997. She claimed later that she never liked this new house and I can understand why. It wasn't the same; it wasn't the one she had shared with my father. Life would never be the same without him and quite honestly I now think that if she could have gone at the same time as he did in 1990 she would have been quite happy.

The island of Barbados in the Caribbean has always featured large within our family life. This is because my mother's cousin Pamela moved to the island and married a Barbadian in the early 1950s. Pamela was a teacher who became headmistress of a very successful comprehensive school for girls in the parish of St Michael, in 1964. As a result she became well known on the island to the extent that she met the Queen during her visits to the island and also appeared on television. In 1990 she was appointed by the Queen to the Order of Barbados in the grade of Barbados Service Star in recognition of her service as an educator. Her husband Harold was a priest and they had two boys (our second cousins as we share the same great-grandfather) one of whom David, the youngest, has followed his father into the ministry and is now Rector on Canvey Island in Essex. The other son, Michael, moved to Toronto in the early '70s and followed his mother into the teaching profession. He has subsequently become a speaker and workshop presenter at educational conferences across Canada to audiences of students and teachers.

Every four or five years the whole family would visit the UK for a few months and we always looked forward to these times. In 1974, we, as a family, managed to visit them in Barbados for five weeks. My parents had never been abroad or flown before so this was quite an event. It was truly a holiday of a lifetime and one that was spoken about afterwards on many occasions. My mother visited again in 1995 when she went with David and his family. By that time Harold had died and Pamela, now retired, was not in the best of health and had not been to the UK for some years, so it was good that the cousins were able to get together again after so long.

Today, even though Pamela and Harold are no longer alive, Barbados will always be special. Due to my mother's tendency to hoard, I have a number of items which she was either sent or bought displaying the name "Barbados" and I cannot bring myself to dispose of them - such is the hold Barbados has on me.

Me at 3 years old with Granddad Percy and Grandma Dorothy in 1957

Below - Mum's beloved bungalow in Brighton, East Sussex 1965

FIRST SIGNS

Winter 2002

The illness must have started to show itself in 2002 but that something was wrong, although we did not know what, only really became more noticeable to us during the month of November. The problem was, however, at that time Mum also had cataracts in both eyes and the things which started occurring in that year we thought were attributable to poor eyesight. This, unfortunately, threw us off the scent as to what was really going on.

Looking back now I realise the first sign was in fact not to do with her eyesight at all. It was the episode concerning changing Mum's car door lock and her car keys. On the driver's door the lock had become faulty and had to be changed, which meant that Mum had to have a new key. As a result she had the original key for the passenger door lock and the new one for the driver's door. Mum could not understand why she could not have one key for both as before, and no amount of explaining got through to her. This first instance of the lack of ability to reason was to be repeated many times over in the coming weeks and months that followed. However, at that time Howard and I were just exasperated with her, I regret to say. Just as she did not understand about the keys, so we did not understand what was happening to her.

The other thing which occurred at about the same time but which we thought was to do with her eyesight was the sudden inability to know her way when driving. My son Jeremy noticed this first because Mum used to pick him up from school most days. On one particular occasion it seemed that Mum was suddenly lost. She continued driving around until finally a certain landmark looked familiar. She would not accept any help on directions from Jeremy, perhaps because she did not want to admit to him, or to herself, that she was lost.

It also became noticeable that Mum did not seem to want to venture far so I had what I thought at the time was a brilliant idea. I suggested to Mum that she might benefit from having a cat for company. She was not keen at first but I was not prepared to give up and eventually we visited the RSPCA and Mum chose a ginger tom which she named "Sandy". Years ago we had had a cat by the same name and although I suggested other names only the name Sandy would do. Of course later it became obvious as to why. People with dementia revert back to their past and even display some likes and mannerisms from the times when they were much younger. Sandy had been a much loved cat so this new cat must have the name Sandy. At that time I did not like the idea. For the life of me I could not understand why this cat could not have its own identity! Unfortunately, it would not be long before I would regret that Mum ever had this animal.

It was becoming obvious that things were not right inasmuch as Mum obviously had a memory problem but even then, due to the cataracts, the seriousness of it had still not fully dawned on us. We obviously had concerns about her driving but were powerless to stop her due to her denial that anything was wrong. This is another feature of dementia which can be present in many who suffer from it.

Christmas became the start of the turning point for us. Cousin David visited, and shortly after arriving told us he thought Mum was ill. He was distressed that Mum, who, for as long as he could remember punctuated her day by making tea, was confused by the process when she came to make him one. In view of everything that had been happening up to then and knowing that David, as a priest, would have come in contact with people with dementia, I realised he must be right. As soon as the Christmas holiday was over I rang the doctor's surgery and made an appointment for 3 January. The GP immediately arranged for Mum to be seen by a specialist but, as it turned out, this appointment did not happen until May. As a result we coped with the situation for five months without a diagnosis or indeed any external help or advice at all. We muddled along on our own trying to understand and deal with what was happening. Perhaps we should have been more insistent on getting an earlier appointment but at the time we accepted that there was a waiting list. In the NHS this was the norm and I thought we had no choice, which, in fact, probably was the case.

Spring 2003

Despite the fact that dementia seemed to be a possibility, as we knew so little about the illness then, we still thought her eyesight explained some of the things which were happening. For instance, on one occasion Mum went to the doctor's surgery and found it closed. She then told me that, on returning to her car, she saw two people sitting in the front seat with covers over their heads. At the time I questioned her closely on what she meant – but subsequently I learned, when dealing with a person with dementia, one should avoid this because such questions can be too hard to answer. It was only later that we realised she must have been mistaking the head rests in the car for real people – but again we believed this was her eyesight playing tricks. As we later came to learn, one of the effects of dementia in some people is that they hallucinate and see things which are not actually there. Another example was her accounts of the visits my Dad made to her. She would describe him sitting in a particular chair but complain that he would not talk to her and often had a cover over his head. We simply did not know what to make of this. For us it was quite unsettling and so we decided the best thing would be not to engage her in conversation but to try to change the subject. We tried to do the same thing with the story of the two children who used to visit her. She would often relate how they had been at her house playing and that she had fed them, and even that sometimes they would not go home. On one occasion I received a call from the police because Mum had dialled 999 to report the fact that these children would not leave her house. I confirmed to them that Mum was ill and when I rang her she told me that, as they would not leave, she had locked the door, so now they couldn't get out, but that she did not want to be held responsible for keeping them so had rung the police.

I suppose there was some confused logic here somewhere but the fundamental point of course was that these children existed only in her mind, although at the time we thought her eyesight was something to do with it as well. Mum never gave these children names although we did get the impression they were two boys. Only much later did it dawn on us that these boys were probably my brother and I when we were young – but we never did find out from Mum. It is said that people with dementia revert back to their past life for means of security particularly when they come to realise that things are changing. Perhaps it was the two of us she was seeing, playing up just as we did in the old days!

Mum's confusion over the time of day became a problem when she had appointments meaning she would often arrive much too early at the hairdresser's or the dentist's. She also very quickly lost the ability to deal with anything technical. Using the cooker, washing machine, VCR, hi-fi and radio became difficult - and most distressing of all was when she lost the ability to play the piano. I recall the day she told me that she could not do it, but she did not get upset. She seemed to be more mystified than anything else, and because she was in denial that anything was wrong she did not, at least at that time, realise her lack of playing ability was to be permanent.

Being in denial unfortunately featured large throughout the whole of her illness and this brought about its own set of problems. It was also at this time that she stopped attending church to sing in the choir. As she sang the alto line she was finding it extremely difficult to read the music and words at the same time, a not inconsiderable skill at the best of times.

We were lucky that Mum did not have any accidents when trying to use the cooker. On one occasion she forgot about some meat she was cooking until too late so it had to be thrown away. On another occasion, when I arrived Mum informed me that the cooker could not be used as it was smoking. In fact she was not referring to the main cooker but a small tabletop oven. When I opened the door I found the plate which belonged in the microwave together with two pairs of oven gloves. When I moved the gloves they fell apart having turned in part to ash. Of course I had no idea how long they had been in there and nor did Mum and I could not get a sensible answer as to why this oven had been switched on in the first place.

Mum's inability to know the exact time of day also meant we started to receive telephone calls during the night. On one occasion she rang my brother in the middle of the night to say she was ready to be picked up to go to Portsmouth, an arrangement they had made previously and was due to happen later that day. We later learned that it was always best not to talk about arrangements too far in advance because Mum would become anxious about missing whatever was arranged, due to her increasing inability to know the time.

The cat had also become a problem and not in the way I could have foreseen. At first he had appeared quite docile and friendly, which he was. Unfortunately, due to Mum's condition, she did not always pay him the attention he wanted and perhaps misunderstood his actions as well. One of the consequences of this was that he would scratch her to get her attention. This would be bad enough if this was on her hand, but he would scratch her legs as she walked about. The skin on Mum's shins was very thin so these scratches would become open places which eventually had to be dressed by a nurse at the community hospital. At that time we were having to attend the hospital, the doctor and the dentist on quite a frequent basis, so I could not believe that this was going to be another regular appointment that would have to be kept in order for her legs to be redressed every few days. This problem, coupled with the fact that Sandy was bringing mice into the house (which according to Mum used to run up the curtains), meant I was eventually forced to broach the subject of taking him back to the RSPCA. At first Mum became tearful when discussing this idea although she did acknowledge that it would be for the best. Later however, and quite unexpectedly, Mum told us the hospital had said the cat should go, having forgotten, I think, that I had ever mentioned it before. She still did not like the idea and was not happy with the hospital staff for suggesting it. However it did make sense because of the extent of the problem with her legs. When the day arrived to take him back, which I had been dreading, Mum in fact was not tearful at all, for which I was very thankful.

Yet another symptom of this illness manifested itself at this time, and once again we did not understand. Mum had become suspicious of other people, particularly her neighbours. She started believing that they were entering her house to remove items which belonged to her. I now know such ideas can stem from failing memory, or an inability to recognise people, or just the need we all feel to make sense of what is happening around us – but at that time, I had not realised this. Mum would use this to explain why things went missing in the house when she couldn't find something – a frequent occurrence. People with dementia may deliberately hide objects to keep them safe and then forget where they are, or indeed that they have hidden them at all. The reason for doing this may be partly due to feelings of insecurity and a desire to hold on to the little that they still have. Certainly this was how Mum appeared to be behaving. She would put an item somewhere so it was safe and could not be found by anybody else and then later not be able to find it herself – and so become convinced it was lost or had been stolen.

One day she could not find her make-up and she told me she felt like knocking on her neighbours' door to ask if they thought they had the right to take it. "It makes me so cross," she said. A day later she complained that during the previous night after going to bed she thought she heard them moving things around including her make-up. Losing things like this was just another problem to be coped with and happened on an almost daily basis. However, Mum was always convinced that she was not at fault and these incidents often became quite frustrating to deal with.

Patience is a virtue and when having close contact with someone who is suffering from dementia you need it in abundance. I did my best but was not always successful, I know. Everyone has their limits and of course at this point we were still quite ignorant about the effects of dementia. Moreover, Mum's actual condition had still to be diagnosed. If something went missing it was either my fault, I had moved it, or the neighbours had been in and done it, or my father was responsible. She complained that on one occasion she went into the spare bedroom only to find Dad had been looking through the bank statements and left them all over the floor. On these occasions she could be quite accusing in her behaviour and yet at other times she would be very different. One day she expressed her worry about spending money which she believed belonged to Dad – i.e. the pension she received as his widow, and feared she was acting illegally by keeping it. As a result she talked about sending the money back. Then she was concerned about where Dad was getting *his* money from and contemplated giving him some money. As for the neighbours coming into her house, she eventually decided that the only way to deal with it was to write a note and put it through their door asking them to stop. Firstly, of course, nothing like this was happening – but in addition she delivered the note to the wrong house!

Dealing with finances was also becoming a problem and I offered to sit down with her to look through her cheque book stubs and statements as perhaps not surprisingly, under the circumstances, she had got herself in a muddle. One outcome of this exercise was my discovery that she had taken out a loan of £1000 some time during 2002. It appeared that the bank concerned had tried to take instalments from her account but had been unable to do so due to insufficient funds. As a consequence they had started sending Mum letters to which she had not responded. The biggest mystery, however, was that it did not appear Mum had ever received the loan into her account. She could not tell me anything about it, other than that she wanted to cancel it. I approached the bank and explained the situation. They agreed that the cheque they had issued had not been cashed, and were willing, under the circumstances, to cancel the arrangement. I later found the cheque in question in a drawer, hidden under some papers. As a consequence of this she agreed for me to become a joint signatory on her bank account which then enabled me to have some control without taking over completely. I don't know now what prompted her but suspect it was purely her interest in all matters financial that in 1997 Mum wisely put in place an enduring power of attorney. This arrangement meant should Mum, at a later date, lose the ability to manage her own affairs my brother and I would be able to deal on her behalf. At this time in 2003, I did not want to have to register the power of attorney until it was really necessary, so becoming a joint signatory on the account was a compromise and worked well.

Security was another issue of concern. Mum would fall asleep in the chair during the evening and with the lounge curtains open could be clearly seen by any callers at the front door. At the same time the back door would be unlocked and access to the rear of the house was relatively easy and one could enter the house almost unnoticed.

Luckily nothing did arise as a result of these incidents but when one day I visited to find Mum was out and the front and back doors wide open, I knew we were coming to the point where she would have to move to somewhere that would be more secure.

It was whilst we were waiting for the appointment with the consultant that Mum had her first cataract operation. She understood well enough what was to happen and was quite prepared to undergo the operation. Although Mum had cataracts in both eyes and had to wait several more months, as is usual in these cases, for the second eye to be done, this first operation appeared to make little difference to her eyesight. It transpired that this was because she also was suffering from macular degeneration. This is the leading cause of vision loss in people over 65 in the UK. The exact cause has not yet been established and there is currently no known cure. As the population continues to age it does have the potential to become an even greater problem which is why research to prevent, delay and treat this condition is necessary. A person with this problem loses sight in their central field of vision but peripheral vision remains unaffected. This means that most people can still walk around, dress and perform normal daily tasks. There are a number of risk factors which predispose someone to this disease. These include age, diet and nutrition, smoking and also gender. Being a woman over 75 doubles the chances of developing the disease compared to a man of the same age. So, despite the operation, because of this disease, Mum's eyesight was not improved and I was still left wondering if some of Mum's problems were caused by poor eyesight rather than because she was suffering from anything else.

LIFE CHANGES

Summer 2003

Any thoughts of this kind were finally dispelled after Mum had a brain scan prior to the long-awaited hospital appointment. The consultant confirmed that Mum was suffering from the early stages of vascular dementia. Alzheimer's disease is the most common cause of dementia, comprising approximately 55% of all cases of dementia. It is a disease which affects the chemistry and structure of the brain leading to the death of brain cells. Vascular dementia is another form of dementia where the brain cells die due to the interruption of the oxygen supply to the brain. The death of the brain cells can cause the symptoms of vascular dementia and can occur either suddenly, following a stroke, or, as in Mum's case, over time through a series of small strokes. The consultant decided to prescribe the drug *Aricept* which, although expensive, had been approved to be given under the NHS for patients in the early stages of dementia and in fact was the first drug to be licensed in the UK specifically for this illness. However, we found out later that in fact not all health authorities in the country prescribe it because of the cost, so we counted ourselves lucky at the time.

Drugs like this one work by supplying an important chemical called *acetylcholine*. As is the case with every drug there can be side effects, including fatigue and loss of appetite, but the important point to note about drugs like *Aricept* is that they will not cure dementia. What they can do is stabilise some of the symptoms for a limited period of time. In Mum's case we noticed a reduction in the hallucinations she experienced. She also appeared to be more aware of the time of day and was less apt to become frustrated about some things she could no longer do. She also lost the upsetting behaviour of being suspicious of others. Overall, this drug helped her maintain some independence for longer than would otherwise have been the case. This is why, at the time of writing, the current decision of NICE, the National Institute for Clinical Excellence, is wrong, in my view, in deciding to refuse this treatment to those in the early stages of dementia.

The argument against the use of the drug is cost but there is the other side of the coin. How much more costly will it be for the country to have to support dementia patients in other ways because they cannot live independently for as long as they could if these types of drug were available to them? It is true that not all patients show any beneficial effects, but even if it is a relatively small improvement in some people this has to be better for all concerned than allowing people to deteriorate more quickly when there is a chance they can be helped, even if on a temporary basis. Although dementia does reduce a person's life, people with Alzheimer's disease can potentially live up to ten years so anything which can help reduce the effect of the symptoms for a period of time must be a good thing, both for the patients themselves and their families/carers.

I think it is true to say we were relieved to finally have a diagnosis. It at least meant we could plan for the future as far as that would be possible. What perhaps became more upsetting and ultimately difficult to deal with, as time passed, was Mum's refusal to believe there was anything wrong with her.

Cousin David had previously raised the subject of warden-assisted housing for Mum and this idea was also suggested by the consultant when Mum was confirmed to be suffering from dementia. We decided to look around for a flat which we hoped would be appropriate. It was not easy, particularly as Mum had a fear of heights which had worsened in the last few years, so that now she would not even entertain the idea of any flat unless it was on the ground floor. We did eventually find one in Woking which was central, and meant Mum could walk into the town and get to the doctor and dentist without having to rely on transport. This was important because we had decided to sell Mum's car. She was not particularly pleased about it but luckily for us did not object to the idea either. The consultant had confirmed she should not drive and Mum was aware (albeit secretly I think) that driving was becoming a problem for her. We sold it very quickly to a friend of ours who still has the car to this day.

The flat we had found consisted of a lounge, kitchen, bedroom and bathroom. There was a communal laundry and also a lounge where residents could meet each other and/or their visitors. It was double glazed and there was a patio door which later became a problem because of the way it had to be opened. However, this difficulty would prove useful because as Mum's illness progressed it meant it would not be easy for her to leave it open or unlocked by mistake. Although this flat was vacant and the people buying her house did not have a place to sell themselves, the whole process took much longer than I envisaged. So it was not until the end of August that Mum moved, and this unfortunately coincided with my brother's holiday. It couldn't be helped but I had not realised how difficult and stressful the move would be. This was in part because naturally Mum could not be much help. She had packed some things herself, but not necessarily appropriately, which meant it had to be re-done. On the actual day of the move she was equally unable to assist and just hovered on the sidelines, as it were, making comments. As I was on my own I was pleased I had arranged for a removal firm to undertake the move rather than us doing it ourselves. I would have preferred Mum to have been completely out of the way on the day, but she would not agree to this idea at all!

Before the move we had managed to dispose of a few items which we knew there would not be room for including her piano which now resides at my house. However, Mum did possess a large number of books and photo albums which had to end up in boxes. After the move into the flat we found it completely congested with them. It took months before all of these could be emptied, but that was a minor problem. By far the biggest difficulty to overcome was Mum's failure to accept her new surroundings. Although we had visited the flat three times after our offer had been accepted in May I had not appreciated that due to her memory loss, she might not remember much about it and what it was like. At least that is how it appeared the following day when I was summoned by the warden because Mum was very upset. I arrived to find her crying and in a very anxious state.

I soon discovered that she did not know why she was in this place, she did not like it, it was not her idea, it was all my doing and she wanted to go home. Nothing I said really made a difference and it led to the incident of throwing her keys at me. What made it worse (if indeed this was possible) was all this happened in front of the warden. We did eventually manage to calm her down – but to say she was unhappy is an enormous understatement. We tried to make the point that it can take time to get used to a new home and when we next visited the consultant she made exactly the same point. The problem of course was that we were not dealing with someone who could really understand and appreciate this fact. As far as she was concerned she didn't like the flat and it was not her idea to move there. She simply could not appreciate that she was better off in this flat. This was due to her illness and to her continued denial that there was anything wrong with her. In her eyes, if anybody had a problem it was me, not her.

Autumn and Winter 2003

Over the coming months we tried to do all we could to reassure Mum and make the place feel like home. Even though I thought she might only live there for about two years I decided that it was still worth trying to make the place feel like hers in the hope that this would help her to settle down and become used to this new environment. As a consequence we re-carpeted the flat throughout with her choice of carpet. We changed the old-fashioned light fittings in the lounge and bedroom and replaced her old sideboard with a built-in unit which had shelves for all those books and photo albums. Her existing bed was rather large for the room so we bought a single one which again she chose, together with replacement bedding. The lounge was double aspect and the glass in one small side window had become so cloudy that you could not see out through it, so we had this window replaced. As the taps in the bathroom were old and difficult to turn these were changed, and finally the existing storage heaters were replaced with up-to-date ones which had improved heating controls. Despite all this, if I am honest, I think it made little underlying difference to how she felt about the flat and I was probably very naïve to think it would do so. Although we had no major upsets as on the first day, there would often be a comment on how much she hated it there and that she would like to move, preferably to a bungalow! We had lived in a brand new bungalow when we moved to Brighton. It was not far from the cliffs, and Mum had loved every minute of living there. She was very sad to leave when my father's job did not work out, and we returned to Surrey. I don't think she ever recovered properly from the disappointment - hence her continued life-long desire to move to a bungalow at some point. It was not to be.

I bought her a cassette tape recorder, record player and CD player with a set of speakers so that she could play the many tapes, records and CDs she possessed. I had hoped the controls on each would be straightforward enough for her to cope with and sometimes she did manage to operate the tape recorder and CD player successfully. The record player however was much more of a challenge. Overall, there were few occasions she would initiate playing music herself and it would only be when Howard or I visited that these items would be used. Similarly, the radio was never switched on either, and this was a significant change because Mum used to be an avid Radio 2 listener. I can hear her now whistling (she was a terrific whistler but only in private!) or singing along to the songs being played by Jimmy Young on his daily radio programme. These days, if I put the radio on, it just seemed to annoy her rather than give any pleasure.

As cooking was out of the question we arranged through her doctor for her to receive meals on wheels. Perhaps not surprisingly she did not enjoy these meals and I did think the quality was variable. However, it was a hot meal delivered to her door and was one less thing to have to worry about. It also meant she had contact with somebody, even if only briefly, if she did not venture out on any particular day. I had bought her an electric hotplate which had two burners so that if she, or we, wanted to cook something in a saucepan we could do so. For her it was safer and much easier to use.

During this period my brother and I developed a pattern of visiting so that he would normally take her shopping once a week and I would visit on a Saturday afternoon and take her out to lunch, as well visit during the week. I also spoke to her by phone every lunch-time. I used to pace the car park at work during these rather strange conversations that often made little sense, but as I was outside nobody would overhear. Mum also came to each of us on alternate Sundays for lunch. Every other Saturday we would take her to the hairdresser, which was always an outing she enjoyed. She had been going to this particular hairdresser for years and she knew them all and just as importantly, they knew her.

Mum had her second cataract operation in October but again, and as expected, there was not much change in her sight. Mum stayed the night at my house after the operation but chose not to stay any longer than that. It was interesting to note that although she said she hated her flat she never wanted to take advantage of being away from it when the chance came up. Whether this was because she felt more secure with her own things around her despite the surroundings I could not work out. As before, drops were required to be put into her eye twice a day for several days following the operation. This time a district nurse visited to do one lot and Howard and I shared the task of doing the second one. Whilst this all went fairly well it was nonetheless such a pity that the desired outcome was not achieved – that she would never enjoy improved vision. It seemed this was simply not possible.

Mum and Dad looking their best in 1982

MOUNTING EFFECTS

Spring and Summer 2004

Mum's world started to shrink. She refused to go to church as a member of the congregation, but never gave an explanation as to why. It could have been to do with the fact that she knew she was ill and could not face all the people she knew. If this was the case she was either too proud to say so, or it was her being in denial which prevented her from being honest.

We tried to encourage her to attend functions in the communal lounge such as Bring and Buy sales, or afternoon tea so that she would meet some of the other residents, and this she would do occasionally. They held an exercise class each week and Mum attended this regularly and appeared to enjoy it. She had always liked keeping fit in her younger days and this really appealed more than anything else. She could not abide playing games of any description such as cards so it was useless suggesting that she went to a beetle drive. There were a few friends who would make contact and visit periodically and perhaps take her out but otherwise she did become quite excluded socially, despite my best efforts. To a large extent her world was becoming confined to her family. Apart from the added pressure this brought on us, I felt this situation was not helping her overall condition and that she was not getting the mental stimulation which I felt she needed now more than ever. Probably, in the back of my mind, I was hoping that such activity might stave off the advance of the illness or even keep it at bay. On reflection I know now this was a forlorn hope.

Mum was starting to have difficulty not just knowing the time of day but also the day of the week. At first it wasn't that she could not tell the time by looking at the clock, it was because she did not believe what it said. You could tell her endlessly that the time was correct but it made no difference. Equally, she did not believe the date shown on her daily newspaper. She simply refused to believe it. This brought added problems when having to attend appointments. If Mum did not know what the day was or the time of day there was no possibility of her turning up on the right day for an appointment. As a result of this we had to change our regime. Instead of making sure she had not forgotten an appointment by ringing her up on the day and just before the appointed time, we had to escort her. This, however was helpful because increasingly she could not be relied upon to say accurately what happened at an appointment.

Mum had been venturing out on her own to walk into the town and although she managed to get there without getting lost, coming back was often a different matter. She refused to use any of the community transport available which was probably just as well as she would have been unlikely to be ready at the appointed time. She came to dislike traffic and was almost frightened of busy roads and this fear became another obstacle preventing her from getting out and about.

Autumn 2004

Knowing the time of day and day of the week was becoming worse so that eventually she did could not understand the clock at all. As a result of this she became more disorientated and the difference between day and night became more confusing to her. Some time previously I had purchased a talking clock on the recommendation of the mental health team at St. Peter's Hospital who did visit Mum on a couple of occasions even though they were not welcome! This clock had just two buttons to press, one which was for the day of the week and the other the date. This was fine except that she never really understood why she had it, and so never used it as I had intended. Even if she was aware she did not know the time, she did not remember that she possessed the talking clock and so did not use it.

The one result of not knowing the time was still having the curtains drawn in the mornings, and on other occasions when I visited at, say, 7 p.m. finding her in bed, fast asleep, probably having been there for some time. The other effect this had was that both Howard and I started to receive calls during the night. She would ring in the early hours perhaps thinking it was a Sunday, and wanting to know when she was going to be collected for lunch. Very occasionally she would display some insight into her condition. On one occasion when she realised she had missed a few people's birthdays she said she must be bad not being able to remember them. However, these moments of lucidity were relatively rare. For much of the time she was still in complete denial that anything was wrong with her. It was everyone else who had a problem! Although her mixing day and night did not happen all the time it did mean that this was one more obstacle which prevented her from leaving her increasingly small world.

The move to warden-assisted housing was necessary, and did mean she was more secure, but she still had to cope with using a washing machine. From what I was able to gather other residents used to help when she got stuck and even the warden might assist at a push. She did become quite frustrated at times about it but nonetheless all the while the implication was that it was the machines rather than her understanding of how they worked that was the cause of her difficulties. It would have been easy to have taken this task away from her, but I felt it was necessary that all the time she could get by doing it herself, even with the help of others, she was retaining a bit of independence. It also gave her something to think about and do and meant she had to leave her flat and converse with some of the other residents.

My brother and I attended a course run by the local branch of the Alzheimer's Society. It was run over six weeks during which time various topics were covered that included: information on the illness, recognising the reasons for unusual behaviour, details of the brain and its behaviour, understanding and respecting the person with dementia, paying care home fees and details of the drug treatments. There were also workshop sessions on how to recognise dementia, what it feels like for the person with dementia, and how carers might look after themselves. The course as a whole was extremely useful and provided information which in some respects we wished we had known in that five month period before Mum was diagnosed. It would have increased our understanding about what was happening to Mum and perhaps enabled us to help her more effectively at that time.

We visited the consultant every three months and an appointment was due. On previous occasions I had found these consultations very difficult. Mum would clam up and not respond to the questions she was asked and I then found myself, by default, answering for her. This appointment was no different but the consultant did manage to get Mum to do the memory test because I think Mum treated it as a game. Apart from this, however, Mum disliked these appointments. Her manner was that of someone who couldn't really see the relevance of the questions she was asked. Perhaps this was yet another indication of the attitude of denial that her illness existed. Or was it rather evidence of her determination not to be beaten by the illness?

Perhaps nothing illustrated her attitude to the illness more than the occasion when the doctor started a memory test by asking her to remember three words: 'cat', 'cup' and 'ball'. At the end of the test she was asked what these words were and she accurately remembered two out of the three. On getting home she asked me what the words were because by then she had forgotten. She responded by laughing and saying "I must write those words down so I remember them for next time". The implication here was that if she remembered the words next time, it would show the doctor there was nothing wrong with her and so justify her position that we were making a fuss for nothing.

Howard and I with Mum on her 75th birthday in 2002

LEARNING TO COPE

Winter 2004

Since Mum's move to the flat we were aware she had not taken a bath. She used to tell me she had a stand-up wash and I am sure this was the case. However there is no substitute for a bath or shower and taking into account as well her social exclusion I had the idea of trying to kill two birds with one stone. I had been aware for a while of local amenities which provided bathing facilities and chiropody, amongst other things. My plan was that if I could get Mum to agree to visit one of these for the purpose of bathing and having her feet done, things might develop to an extent where she might join in with other events that were held. I happened to know the manager of one of them and agreed with her a date and time to visit. It did not go quite according to plan because the manager was unavailable and although Mum and I had lunch I had to make excuses to Mum as to why we continued to hang around for a while. Eventually, the manager turned up and showed us round. Unfortunately I was more or less thwarted at the end of the visit when told that, as Mum lived in Woking, she was outside the catchment area for that particular centre. In any case my plan was stopped dead in its tracks, not because we would have to go somewhere else necessarily, but because Mum refused to go and be helped to bathe. It was as simple as that. To be honest I can't say I would relish the idea either but this episode demonstrated to me yet again Mum's total refusal to recognise that she needed help of this kind.

Thinking of how to get Mum out of the flat I suggested we visit her sister-in-law who lives near Swanley in Kent. This is the relative who was a witness at their wedding in 1977. My uncle had died in the late 80s but Aunty Alice was still going strong. She is a lovely bubbly lady, full of life and vigour. She was pleased to see Mum as was Mum to see her and I was delighted I had made the effort to take Mum, not only because it was a day out but because I had the feeling this might be the last time they would have the opportunity to meet up. Regretfully, this proved to be the case.

It was becoming noticeable that Mum's condition was getting worse. Apart from mixing up days and times which had been happening for a while on and off, it was becoming apparent that Mum was starting to see certain people again. She also started to believe that people were coming into her flat at night so she must hide some of her possessions such as her handbag and, of all things, the biscuit barrel! (Well, she always did like biscuits.) For some time she had been missing certain TV programmes, because she did not know the correct time. Not that she believed that was the case – it was the BBC and ITV's fault for messing about with the programme timings! The weekly shop also became more of a challenge to the point where she did not seem that interested in what to buy. However, by this time she was not eating much more than was provided by meals on wheels so the amount of shopping being purchased was decreasing anyway.

A few weeks previously, I had bought tickets for a carol concert at Guildford Cathedral. This is something Mum used to enjoy going to and I thought it would be an outing which still might bring her some pleasure. Admittedly, if I had not bought the tickets in advance I might have had second thoughts about going, bearing in mind Mum's deterioration. However, I hoped that for a couple of hours it would be a useful diversion from the norm - something different to do. It turned out to be a disaster.

My first mistake was going on my own with her. This might not have been a problem except that when we arrived at the Cathedral I wanted to park as close as I could but so many people had already arrived there were very few spaces left near the Cathedral. Luckily I did find one space but it was a bit tight which meant Mum had to get out of the car to allow me to park. This proved easier said than done. Firstly, I had to get out of the car, walk round to her side and help her out. I then needed to find somewhere she could stand and wait for me whilst I reversed into the space. This sounds straightforward but Mum unfortunately did not fully understand what I was doing, and as I reversed, she started to walk towards the car. I was conscious of other cars coming and concerned that she would walk into their path. I soon realised that this exercise would have to be repeated when we left so I spent the whole of the first half of the concert worrying about how I was going to get Mum back in the car without leaving her on her own again. I thought there might be someone we knew there whom I could ask to assist. This could have been a possibility but during the first half it was obvious Mum was not happy. We were quite a long way back so she couldn't really see and she did not appear to be enjoying what was being sung because her ability to concentrate for any length of time had reduced considerably (something else I had underestimated!) Because of all of this I suggested we should leave during the interval and she made no complaint about this. However, having managed to get her back in the car without mishap I realised that in my stressed state I had left my jacket behind in the Cathedral. So I had to park again, hoping Mum would stay put, and dash back in. Luckily the second half of the concert hadn't started. It was only once back in the car and driving away that I was able to breathe a huge sigh of relief.

Despite Mum's worsening condition she did want to make the trip to David's celebration of twenty-five years as an ordained priest. There was to be a church service followed by lunch and although I did not tell her, Michael – David's brother – was also going to be there. The journey to Canvey Island is quite long and I think Mum found that tiring in itself. We made it and of course it was great for her to see David and his family, Michael with his partner Larry, and also her brother Ken who had come down from his home in Norfolk. Mum was, however, noticeably quiet and did not comment much on the proceedings at the time or indeed afterwards but I think that the important thing was that she did manage to go, and was able to see her side of the family for what would be the very last time.

Over Christmas and into January, Mum was very quiet and more vacant than usual. She lost any enthusiasm which before she had shown at times, and her mood became quite flat. She came to us on Christmas Day and I have a wonderful photograph of her laughing almost hysterically at something I had said but now you would not say it particularly looks like my mother. She was no longer interested in the keep fit class which had been the one thing up until then she had looked forward to and enjoyed. I sat in on a class on one occasion. There was only a handful of ladies present and some of them had to remain sitting the whole time. Mum appeared to be one of the more "agile" ones by comparison and the person running the class had the knack of making the whole thing fun, and giving them all a laugh at the same time.

I had arranged an optician's appointment for a check-up and it transpired that Mum was wearing very old glasses and we had not realised it. On finding this out from the optician Mum's exact words were "I must be going bonkers if I did not realise I was not wearing the right ones". This was proof yet again that she did not seem to have any idea what was happening to her or did not want to admit it, at least to me.

It was also noticeable that her disorientation was getting worse even within the confines of her flat. She would get up out of the chair to go to the kitchen but then walk in completely the wrong direction. Sometimes, if she wanted to go to the bathroom, she would walk into the kitchen instead.

The other big problem we had at this time was the medication - not only ensuring she was remembering to take it, but also that she was taking the correct dosage. To be honest it should not have been that difficult as it was only one tablet a day although the consultant had also suggested she take cod liver oil and a herbal remedy which is supposed to assist with cognitive decline. So this made three tablets a day. We had bought a tablet dispenser which had days of the week printed on it so that both Mum and we would know whether she had taken a particular day's dosage. Whilst this worked for a while this regime was now starting to fall apart. Mum often had difficulty opening the dispenser compartments at the best of times, but now, when she got it open, the tablets might fall on the floor. She could not then find them, so she would naturally open another compartment and take those instead. From the point of view of us monitoring what she had taken it became a nightmare and we were constantly finding tablets down the side of the chair and on the floor. If you asked her whether she had taken them that day she could not always remember, so it was at this point that we made the decision that we would have to visit her every day and actually administer the tablets ourselves.

On 26 January Mum had an appointment with the consultant. This time I decided that rather than see the consultant together, it would be best if Mum was seen on her own on the basis that perhaps she might be more inclined to talk if I was not in the room. This did not work. Mum was prickly and quite hostile towards the consultant regarding her condition and talking about it. However, the consultant did manage to carry out the memory test which confirmed that her condition was worse as she only scored a total of fifteen compared with double that score during the previous appointment three months earlier. The upshot of this appointment was that the consultant decided Mum no longer had the capacity to say no – in other words – to make decisions, and that she had become more vulnerable to abuse and being abused. I was told to consider finding a home for her, preferably one that specialised in the elderly mentally ill (EMI). It was also agreed that the dosage of *Aricept* would be increased to try to counteract the current decline in Mum's condition as far as this was possible.

Mum had developed a tendency to lean to the right when sitting or standing. We were not sure at this time if she had suffered a small stroke. Dressing now became an issue with jumpers on back to front, no socks and possibly, on occasion, no underwear. The odd accident was also occurring but luckily at first she seemed to be aware of it and would change her clothes when necessary.

Mum had still not returned to the weekly exercise class. It was only very gentle exercise but even so I think Mum definitely benefited from going to it each week. However she started making excuses about why she did not want to go. Looking back now I think it was probably more to do with the fact that she was increasingly confused about the time of day than anything else, but if this was the case she never became upset about missing it – at least not in front of me.
In view of the noticeable changes in Mum's condition I contacted the Dementia Link worker from the Alzheimer's Society. Having attended their course we were aware now of

the assistance they can provide. I felt we had reached the stage where we needed to get an opinion on whether Mum would benefit from having outside assistance from, say, Help the Aged, and also about her attending the Alzheimer's Society's Day Centre. Unfortunately, this arranged visit did not go well as Mum declined to co-operate, maintaining she did not need any help. The Dementia Link worker told me that in these situations the only way forward was to wait until the person became worse, and had less awareness, then it would be easier for the person to agree to be helped. I understood this, and it wasn't the Link Worker's fault, but Mum needed the help now. I was coming to realise that if we could not get that help because Mum continued to refuse it, the possibility of her moving into residential care would have to become a reality much sooner than would otherwise have been the case.

Mum had her usual appointment at the hairdresser but on this occasion things did not go according to plan. When I arrived to collect Mum, the owner told me that Mum had not been able to lean backwards over the basin to have her hair washed, and also had noticed she was leaning when sitting. She wondered if Mum had had a stroke. We never did find out if that was the reason for this inability to sit straight. What was clear was that we now needed some outside help, so I decided to contact Social Services to establish if Mum was eligible for help from them. I was present during this visit and it was obvious to the care manager that Mum was eligible, but again Mum would not agree to anything. Another problem was that although eligible from a needs point of view, Mum was well over the financial limit for help directly from Social Services, so I was given a list of agencies to contact. I was also told that we could claim Attendance Allowance, so this visit was not a total waste of time despite Mum's attempt to dictate otherwise. However, the battle was not over yet.

As a result of Mum's noticeable decline various other incidents occurred. They included her thinking she had been out and had got lost even though she had been at home all the time; removing washing from the wrong machine, taking it to her flat and dumping some on the floor with the rest left in a basket; not eating lunch and leaving it on a chair for "them to eat but they didn't"; and wandering around the corridors refusing to go into her flat because she reckoned it was not hers.

Then there were the conversations about herself and her situation which in part did not always make sense. The following conversation started unexpectedly after I asked her what she was thinking about. She had been sitting in a chair silently for a short while. To my surprise it prompted this response.

Mum: "My last days on earth – will I have to spend them here? All these suggestions that are put to me and they seem to be getting further away from me."
Robin: "What do you mean, that you can't do what you want to do?"
Mum: "Yes, why can't I do things like other people? Still, if you want to kill me giving me those tablets…"
Robin: "They are for your health and well-being. Do you think I wanted you to move here? Don't you think I would have preferred you stay where you were?"
Mum: "Why did you then?"
Robin: "Because the doctor felt it was for the best."
Silence.

Whether this shows that Mum was admitting she had an insight into her illness I cannot be sure. Perhaps if anything the reference to the tablets again suggests she could not admit, did not want to admit, she was ill. These conversations always ended in silence because Mum would eventually not know how to respond. They would only happen very occasionally and so were the only times when there was ever a hint that she knew more than she was letting on. However, at this point, she was generally displaying more confusion and disorientation than ever, even though the tablets (the dreaded tablets) were being taken regularly.

The day in February when Mum refused to enter her flat, I was called by the warden. When I arrived Mum was wandering around the hallway. She told me that she thought No. 5 was someone else's and asked where we were going to move her things to, and where was she going to sleep that night. I managed to persuade her to go back in, and after a while it was almost as though the whole thing had never happened. What prompted this I never found out.

It was also in this month when Mum experienced incontinence in a major way. Two days after the corridor incident, Mum had an accident and my brother luckily happened to arrive soon afterwards. She told him she had been taken by surprise, she hadn't realised she wanted to go etc. A couple of days later I found soiled incontinence pads which had not been disposed of. It was becoming obvious that Mum's condition was getting worse, so I made contact with Age Concern to see if Mum could be visited by one of their carers.

My thinking was that if Mum agreed to this at least someone would be going in and getting her up at the start of the day, giving her breakfast, and helping to create some routine. How long this would last I didn't know but at this stage it was better than nothing. I received a call back and a lady named Pat said she would visit Mum with me in attendance, to discuss what we would like her to do. This happened and

Mum thankfully did not make a fuss. Truth to tell I think she had little energy to object so we agreed Pat should start the following week on Monday 28 February.

On Sunday 27 February I arrived at 9 am to get Mum up. I found her in bed fully clothed, which I don't think was unusual although I was not always there to witness it. I made her change her clothes but could not persuade her to have a wash, another thing which did not happen much, as far as I could tell, despite what she said to the contrary. She would only eat a very small amount of cereal saying she was not hungry. I took her home and she eat some lunch but had very little to say, showed no interest at all in the TV and spent some time sitting with her eyes closed, appearing to be asleep.

The next day Pat visited for the first time. However, according to Mum, she did very little because Mum could not think of anything for her to do. As usual what Mum said and what actually happened were two different things and Pat rang me later to confirm that she had got Mum up, washed and dressed her and given her some breakfast. Apart from this, and washing up, there was nothing else to be done. As far as I was concerned this was good enough and Pat was doing just what I had intended. So far so good.

Howard took Mum for the weekly shop in the early evening as usual. However she showed little interest in choosing items to buy.

I was contacted the following day by a worker at a residential care centre in Kingfield, Woking where we had visited a couple of weeks before. It is for people with dementia and was absolutely ideal. It was all on ground level and was split into 5 separate units which each had their own lounge, kitchen and dining area plus bedrooms for about 12 people.

Unfortunately, they had no vacancies when we visited so we put Mum's name down on a waiting list. When they rang me it was to offer a day centre place only. Mum had always resisted going to a day centre but now her condition was worse I thought maybe we might be able to get her to go. The dementia link worker from the Alzheimer's Society was visiting the following week so I decided to discuss this offer with her first as this was a service which the Society also provides.

Pat rang on Wednesday 2 March to tell me she was having difficulty getting into the flat. Mum had not been able to let her in. Using the entry phone system had always been a problem from the start. Sometimes she managed it but at other times it remained a mystery to her. Due to this Pat was having to ring the warden's bell to ask him to allow her entry, which he was not happy about.

The next day, when I visited in the evening, Mum was complaining of feeling very tired. By this time I was aware that she was not eating her Meals on Wheels lunch, and on this day I found it tipped out on to a magazine in the hall apparently for the cat to eat! Her trousers were on the wrong way round, her hair was unbrushed and she had not had anything to drink since Pat had visited around 9 am that morning. Things were becoming dire.

We now realised that the time for finding a home for Mum to move into was getting ever closer. We had in previous weeks visited three homes but were not entirely happy with any of them, mainly because none matched up to the one we had already found in Kingfield. There was still no vacancy but we were told about a similar home in the same group in Epsom where there might possibly be a room available. Howard rang them and luckily they did have a vacancy so it was agreed we would visit on Saturday. That same evening my wife received a phone call. It was to say that her Aunt Millie, whom we had been visiting regularly in a residential home since 1996, had died suddenly. It was quite a shock and although she had not been in the best of health, it had been nothing life threatening. This home was in Banstead and so it transpired that on Saturday, 5 March we not only visited Appleby House which was to become our mother's new home, but also Fir Tree House, to collect Aunt Millie's effects. Not a day we are ever likely to forget.

Appleby House is very similar to the one in Kingfield and seemed absolutely ideal for Mum. The only problem – it was in Epsom and not Woking. However, it was becoming a case of beggars can't be choosers so we agreed that Mum should spend the day at Appleby so that she could be assessed to ensure it would be right for her.

Pat had rung on Friday 4th to say that the warden was unhappy that Mum was not able to allow Pat entry with the result that he had to be relied upon every day. He told her in no uncertain terms that the establishment was for "independent living". I had already asked if Pat could have a key but it is Age Concern's policy for their staff not to accept door keys for security reasons. We arranged for Pat not to visit on Monday 7 March because of the visit to Appleby House, and she did agree to have a door key as it would only be temporary, on the basis that Mum would be moving imminently.

The visit to Appleby House went without a hitch and it was agreed Mum could move in on Wednesday 9 March. When I say without a hitch I really mean from the home's viewpoint. Mum did not really understand what was happening but frankly at this point I felt it did not matter - we had very little choice but to go through with it. It was the last thing we wanted to do, but events were conspiring against us.

I wonder now what we would have done if Appleby House had not taken Mum at that particular time, but I feel fortunate that we were never put in that position under the circumstances. The following day I felt the need to stay with Mum all day. She seemed very weak and walking was difficult. Pat had made her last visit so at least Mum was up and dressed. However getting to the toilet and sitting was to prove quite a trial and I have to admit I did panic, and rang Appleby House to see if they would accept Mum that day. They understood but said they liked to plan admissions and would rather we waited until the following day as agreed. Of course, having rung and been told no, I wished I had not rung in the first place but I had had a momentary panic and picked up the phone. To say now that I feel some guilt about this period is putting it mildly. I knew there were other people who put up with far worse than we had faced and for much longer. Equally, however the situation was such that to have to continue at Mum's home without effective outside help was becoming impossible and not helped by the attitude of the warden. I knew for a fact that there were other residents who were having care from Age Concern and other agencies all the time. The only difference was, I assume, other residents could use the entry phone system, my mother couldn't, and this was unacceptable to the warden. It was as simple as that.

Had things worked out differently we would have been left with little choice but to make a complaint about what was effectively a form of discrimination. This was not necessary because events were moving quickly but I find it difficult to forgive this response to someone who was ill and so unable to help herself. Whilst the place may be for "independent living" a more lenient and sympathetic approach would not have gone amiss at a time which was very stressful, not least for our mother.

I had arranged to meet my brother at the flat first thing on the morning of Wednesday 9 March. I arrived first to find Mum sprawled across the bed but with her feet on the floor. It seemed she managed to get to the bathroom but on returning to the bedroom more or less fell backwards onto the bed but was unable to move her legs from a sitting position. With Mum in this position and Howard still to arrive I decided there was nothing for it but to join her so we both lay on the bed in the same position looking at the ceiling with me trying as best I could to make a joke out of it. Luckily Mum did see the funny side and it wasn't long before Howard turned up not expecting, of course, to find what he did! Between the two of us we got Mum to her feet and did our best to wash and dress her. She was aware she was going somewhere and as we didn't want to tell any lies we did say we were going to Appleby House but she didn't understand (perhaps fortunately). It was a terrible position to be in and the staff were well aware of how we were feeling, having witnessed this many times before with new arrivals. They settled Mum into one of the five units and we did not stay too long on this occasion.

Subsequently Mum was moved to another unit as they felt the first one was too noisy for her. So it was, that on our next visit we found her in "Pippin". Seeing her in the lounge with one or two others just did not seem right. She looked out of place. She was pleased to see us and asked where we had been – a question that became a regular one at the start of our visits. She seemed stronger already, and in a brighter mood which I believed was due to her eating and drinking now being closely supervised.

NEW HOME

Spring 2005

During the time Mum was at Appleby House we were able to get to know some of the other residents. There was a lovely Welsh lady who had mobility problems as well as suffering from dementia. She was one whom you could have a conversation with, after a fashion, but the conversations between her and Mum were unfathomable! Neither could understand the other but it did not seem to bother them at all. Then there was the elderly chap who believed Mum was his wife. This did not please her at all and she always waved him away anytime he came close. Interestingly, she did understand the mistake he was making and as a consequence had no patience with him at all.

During our visits we would encourage Mum to walk from "Pippin" to the front of the building and back again, or, if it was fine, go for a walk in the garden. During these trips we would often bump into Mary. The very first time I met her she had me completely fooled. She spoke firmly, convincingly and with authority. Every word she uttered you could understand. She would often tell you that she had been a nurse in Sheffield and how she longed to go back there and that she would one day. So convincing was she that I genuinely believed, for a few minutes, on that first meeting, that she was a visitor to Appleby. It was only when she mentioned that she was expecting her mother shortly to arrive to take her home that the penny dropped. Every occasion after that at least when I was with Mum, Mary always made a point of talking to Mum, often giving her a hug and telling her how beautiful she was. Mum's response would either be one of bemusement or impatience, depending on her mood at the time. Yes, sometimes Mary was a bit of a nuisance, often turning up at the wrong times and outstaying her welcome, but she meant well, and had an obvious love of people. It was tragic that she should have been so afflicted with this illness and I often wondered what it would have been like to have met the "old" Mary.

"Going home." How we came to dread hearing those two words. Everybody you spoke to wanted to "go home" and why wouldn't they? None of them understood why they were at Appleby, least of all Mum. These words were either said as part of a question, such as "When am I going home?" or as a statement "I am going home tomorrow". It was almost like a mantra, and unfortunately infectious. This made visiting tricky, especially when the time came to leave.

We were advised not to visit too frequently in the first few weeks because of this, but our experience was that the lapse of time did not make it any easier. Mum would go through the motions of saying goodbye but then when we walked away she would immediately rise from her chair to walk with us. On one occasion I decided to be tactical. I would kiss her, say goodbye and then, before she knew it, would be out of the lounge door closing it swiftly behind me. I would then walk smartly or break into a run in order to round the corner so I was not visible from the door. Well, the first part of this strategy worked well. I was out of the door and away but what I didn't bargain for was her calling out my name. She had managed to get to the door, open it, and, although I was out of sight, still call me - so I returned (my first mistake). I tried to persuade her to go back into the lounge but she was having none of it so I decided she could walk a little of the way with me and then I would leave her in the hope she would turn back. Again, she was not going to be so deflected. I said goodbye and walked quickly away only to realise that she was following me. I knew I had to keep going or else the situation would get even more out of hand. The actual front door of the building is security controlled and to get out a four digit number has to be punched into a keypad. Fortunately we had been told the number but this meant I couldn't just walk straight out without stopping. I reached the inner doors and moved through them into the small vestibule, keyed the numbers in and opened the front door. By this time Mum had reached the inner doors but I had to keep going and I didn't look back. However, when I turned round in the car and drove past the front door, Mum was standing there waving to me through the glass. To say I was upset was an understatement. I felt dreadful but not just because of that incident, which I had handled badly and vowed never to do in that way again, but about the whole situation.

I tried to console myself with the thought that she was in the best place and that the last two or three months had confirmed that she needed specialist care that none of us could provide. In the early days of the illness I had toyed with the idea of her coming to live with us but a number of people I spoke to, including our cousin David, were against the idea because of the likely effect it would have on the whole family. David's argument was that professional carers can go off duty after an eight hour shift, but for the family of someone with dementia, there is no break, no respite and no improvement. In my working life a few years ago I was seconded to another department of the local authority to carry out reviews of certain services and one was the service the Council provides for carers. During that review I met a number of people including one man who had given up work to care for his mother. Of course he did have help from Social Services but nonetheless he was there for her all the time and one couldn't help being full of admiration for such an act. Admittedly he did not have a family, as far as I knew and his brother was also on hand to help, but what a completely unselfish act. Much as I loved my mother I could not see there was any way I would have been able to do the same, and yet who knows, if circumstances had been different and I was single perhaps we would not have had to contemplate residential care, or the cost of it.

After Mum left the flat neither Howard nor I wanted to go back there. It was just too much of a reminder of the action we had had to take, and it did not hold any happy memories for us either. Eventually, however, we had to face selling the flat because there was no possibility of Mum returning there. That was certain.

We already knew that Mum would be a "self-funder" as they call it, because she had a property which could be sold. The State only contributes to care home fees when a person's savings are below £20,500. It seems rather harsh that people, who have probably managed their finances carefully should have to pay for their care if they can afford it, whilst those that have no money – perhaps because they have had a great life spending it, are immediately helped by the State if they need care. I cannot help wondering if this is right or fair.

Residential care is not cheap. To stay at Appleby House in 2005 Mum had to pay £676 a week. She was in receipt of Attendance Allowance, but this only amounted to £61 a week - less than 10% of the total weekly amount she had to pay for her care. Many older people would not want it to be any different. Paying their way is what they are used to doing and certainly Aunt Millie, who was in residential care and later in a nursing home for a total of nine years, constantly worried about what would happen if she ran out of funds to pay her monthly care bills. She had a conscience and did not want to be a burden on the State or anybody else. It is true that some people are not fortunate enough to be in a position to pay for care for such a long period of time, if at all. However, Aunt Millie, and many other people just like her, have worked hard all their lives and earned their money. They wisely saved and invested some of their earnings only to see it dwindle away to pay for care, when they are no longer able to look after themselves. Aunt Millie did not have a problem with that, but in my opinion, the fact that some people find dignity in being in a position to pay, does not make the situation acceptable.

We returned to the flat at the end of April to clear it out. We donated most of Mum's furniture to Woking Hospice for them to sell to raise funds. The rest of her belongings were to be stored at my house for the time being. We put the flat on the market on 9 May and were fortunate enough to receive an offer just a week later which we accepted.

Visiting Mum gradually became easier because we tried to time visits so that our departure could coincide with a meal time. I would usually visit twice a week, once after work and again at the weekend. I never knew what I would find on arrival and never could anticipate what might occur during a visit. Mum's room was painted pink with a large bay window and an enormous artificial plant that had pink flowers. There was a washbasin in a unit which could be closed off by double doors, a wardrobe and a chest of drawers with a matching bedside table.

All her clothes had had to be named so that after being laundered staff would know which clothes belonged to which resident. Despite this, however, it didn't always work out that way. On more than one occasion when visiting I would see one or two other residents wearing an item of clothing which I recognised as belonging to Mum. Equally, I particularly recall seeing Mum in a blouse which was not hers and for some reason this blouse stayed with her as she wore it on more than one occasion. Interestingly, this blouse had no name in the back so why had it become part of Mum's wardrobe all of a sudden? I was told that one other reason why clothes get mixed up is because some residents are fond of going into other residents' rooms and helping themselves. The staff do their best to spot this when it happens but are not always successful. On most visits it was not unusual to come across a few residents just wandering around, going from one unit to another and around the hallway. This is how dementia affects some people. Sadly, there always seemed to be one resident who was visibly upset and no amount of consoling made any difference. This was distressing to witness and must have been very difficult for any of their relatives who visited to deal with. It made me realise again that even in our situation, there were always going to be others in a worse position.

In the three months or so Mum was at Appleby House, she only left its confines on two occasions. Once my brother took her for a drive up to Epsom Downs. Unfortunately, it was totally unappreciated - she actually asked him after a short time to take her back. The other occasion was when she and I ventured out for a walk down the road. Appleby House is situated in a road which is very long and straight but also very wide with a path which runs alongside a stream well away from the passing traffic. As Mum had held an increasing dislike of the noise and speed of traffic for some time, this walk seemed ideal. We set off walking at a slowish pace and that was no problem. I tried to point out the various trees and plants along the way which were in flower. She spent some of the time telling me a very convoluted story about a visit she made to somebody's house in the area who was a friend of a member of the Appleby's staff. She had mentioned this to me before and I could honestly not make head nor tail of it but the way she spoke you would have thought that it really had happened. It was about this time when Mum started to have more difficulty in making herself understood so this did not help the situation either with respect to this story or more other important things.

We must have been out walking for about forty minutes. We had turned round to walk back the same way and as we neared Appleby House we crossed the road to enter the driveway. All seemed fine until we were within a few feet of the front door when all of a sudden she pulled away from me and started to walk off. It was totally unexpected but it was clear she had realised where we were heading and decided that was not where she wanted to go! I talked to her and tried to reassure her everything was alright, but it was clear that no amount of encouragement from me was going to make any difference. What was I to do? Very fortunately for me the manager of Appleby House had just appeared out of the building and walked to her car which was parked on the opposite side of the entrance. She was talking to someone but then noticed us and the situation. She quickly walked across to us and with her professional skill persuaded Mum that all was well and we all entered the building together without any further problem. The relief I felt at this point was palpable. I decided then and there I would not venture out again with Mum, at least not in the immediate future. However, little did I know that this would soon become impossible anyway.

THE PARTING

Summer 2005

As Mum was now resident in Epsom she had to change her doctor. Since entering Appleby House Mum had remained on *Aricept* but at the end of May I was told that the doctor had decided she was no longer benefiting from taking this drug and was to come off it. I was given the opportunity to meet the doctor if I wished but at the time I did not consider it necessary as I trusted his professional decision. Had I only known what was to come I might have decided differently - but then hindsight is a wonderful thing.

When someone stops taking a drug like *Aricept* it is known that their condition will deteriorate over a period of four to six weeks until they are no better than someone who has not ever taken the drug. Mum seemed to become worse within days rather than weeks. Had I known this would happen so quickly I would have made more effort to see the doctor for clarification on his reasoning for withdrawing the prescription for *Aricept*. I did know it would not be a drug Mum could take for ever but it would have been helpful to know how he had reached this decision.

The speed of decline in her condition was both breathtaking and distressing. Firstly, her clarity of speech was affected so that she could not hold a meaningful conversation. She talked and we listened but we had to guess what it was she was saying because none of it made sense. As you can imagine this frustrated her deeply, believing as she did that she was perfectly intelligible. This difficulty made visiting her more challenging than ever. Then she developed mobility problems. Walking suddenly became an issue. Firstly, she lost the abililty to walk in a straight line and then could not even put one foot in front of the other. Finally, as if this were not bad enough, she developed the habit of closing her eyes, as if she were drifting off to sleep. At first she would close her eyes for a short period but later she would do this for longer periods making what little communication was possible even more difficult. I did not realise then the fact that this can be a symptom in people who are in the last stages of dementia. However, I had not appreciated fully that this was the stage the illness had reached.

It is true to say that the various symptoms displayed can vary from person to person. Those sometimes displayed by people in the latter stages might be experienced by others who have the illness only moderately and vice versa. From the last visit to Appleby House I made whilst Mum was there I took away the abiding memory of her being helped to the dining table with one carer supporting her from behind and another guiding and holding her arms. Later, when visiting to collect Mum's belongings, I noticed a wheelchair in her room, so it appeared they had had to resort to using this, which did not surprise me in view of what I had witnessed just a few days earlier.

On Friday 29 June at 6 p.m. I received a telephone call from Appleby House. Luckily I was still at work in Leatherhead as the gist of the call was that Mum had had some sort of fit and had been taken by ambulance to Epsom General Hospital. I went straight there and on arrival joined the queue in the Accident and Emergency Centre. This queue moved very slowly but eventually I reached its head and was told to take a seat as Mum was still being assessed by a doctor and I would be called. As nothing had happened after

20 minutes I decided to join the queue again, which was still quite long and still moving slowly. Someone ahead of me had a bleeding head wound and was dripping blood onto the reception counter. Of course this had to be cleaned up but I don't think anyone in the queue expected the one and only receptionist would have to leave her post, get a cloth and bucket, and venture our side of the counter to clean it up herself. Oh, the joys of working for the National Health Service, not to mention the equal joy for us to have to use the service, but they were doing their best, as I was to subsequently find out in the weeks that followed.

Eventually I was allowed through to see Mum. She was in a cubicle, lying on a trolley with bed sides to ensure she did not fall off. With her was a carer from Appleby whom I did not recognise. She was friendly enough but I was immediately concerned that this carer had not taken more interest in preserving my mother's dignity. This is something which is mentioned a great deal with people who have this illness. Respecting the person's dignity is so important when they have lost so much else. I might have been able to excuse this carer if she had not had any experience of dementia, but she worked at Appleby House. This might be a hospital – but that made no difference. The fact was I found Mum wearing one of those awful hospital gowns which ties up at the back. Except in this case it was not tied and as a result one side had slipped down exposing her shoulder, upper arm and breast. I immediately addressed the situation and we sat and waited. It was soon obvious this carer could not wait for ever, and there was no point in her staying now that I was there, so 20 minutes after I arrived she decided to go and we were left on our own.

Mum was lying with her eyes closed and more or less silent. She was not unconscious but equally was not responding when I talked to her. She had a wound on her upper left arm where she had flailed around during the fit. It looked quite nasty and was yet to be properly dressed. There was a bag of clothes on the floor which I later discovered were the ones she had been wearing earlier and which had been cut off her. They were soiled with blood and had to be thrown away. Mum was eventually seen again by a doctor and taken for x-rays. She was gone for about half an hour. Time then passed very slowly. Mum mumbled incoherently and I tried to reassure her by telling her where she was and why, but I could not be certain I was getting through to her.

Finally the decision was made to admit Mum for observation. So at just after 10 p.m. Mum was moved to a ward. For the whole of the time I was with her that evening she did not open her eyes once. It was the worst I had seen her, and I assumed that the fit she had suffered could have been brought on by a stroke, but that evening I was not given any information at all. I reluctantly left her side at around 10.30 p.m. I was reluctant because, although she was not communicating with me, I was nonetheless concerned that she remained totally unaware of where she was, and I did not like to think of her suddenly realising when she was on her own. Later, with the benefit of knowing what was to follow, I came to realise that this awareness of her surroundings would never return and that therefore my concerns were completely unfounded.

At the time of Mum being admitted to hospital my brother was on holiday. Whilst this meant I could not share my worry and concern with him at that point, the fact that I had to visit every day was not a problem. Working in Leatherhead meant I could get to Epsom more quickly and easily than from Woking and this proved to be even more advantageous later on. I will always be very appreciative that I am able to work flexibly. It certainly proved advantageous to me throughout Mum's illness but particularly at this time when she was hospitalised. These days, even where employees are required to work set hours, employers are becoming mindful of work/life balance and that many people do have caring responsibilities. This is why it is becoming increasingly common for businesses to adopt a policy of providing leave for staff who are also carers. A benefit of this type, or flexible working, is invaluable to an employee who has to juggle their work with a caring role.

Howard and I soon discovered that our frequent visits to the hospital were becoming expensive. This was because like many hospitals, Epsom General Hospital charge visitors to park their cars. For this reason, Howard had taken to parking in a side road on his visits but I did not always manage this for several reasons. Firstly, because as I was able to visit more often during the day, there were no spaces in the nearest side roads and secondly I always felt guilty about parking outside someone's house knowing how much they must dislike it. Certainly I did park elsewhere on occasion but most of the time I used the hospital car park where the charges were around £2.50 per visit. I was not happy about this but my priority was visiting my mother and often when I visited at lunchtimes I did not have much time to spare so it was quicker and more convenient to park there than hunt for a space elsewhere. Now with hindsight I wish I had attempted to claim back some of the cost I paid. Why should relatives have to pay in situations where their loved ones have a serious long-term illness? There must be many people who cannot really afford to pay this cost regularly but feel they have no choice. No doubt this income is welcomed by cash-strapped hospitals but it cannot be right that visitors to patients who are terminally ill, for example, should have to pay when, as a natural consequence, their visits are likely to be very frequent and for longer periods of time. In my view there should be a procedure in place for relatives to claim back parking costs from the hospital trust in these circumstances and hospitals should make it known how this can be achieved.

The day after admission I was contacted and told Mum had been moved to another ward in another wing of the hospital. I recognised the name of this wing as the one where Aunt Millie had been hospitalised nine years earlier just prior to her moving into a residential home. I remembered from then that this was not the best part of Epsom Hospital and this was confirmed when I visited later that day. At first sight it looks quite a modern building but on closer inspection it becomes obvious it was probably built at least thirty years ago which although not that old, because of apparent neglect looks much older compared with the other parts of the hospital. It reminded me of one of the buildings at my old school which was built in the 1960s. Since our last visit to the hospital in 1996, this wing had not improved, particularly the public areas of the building which were scruffy and run down, as though nobody cared. The design of the building and the layout of the wards with long straight corridors and rooms leading off them did not help either. However, looking on the bright side, it was only a three storey block, not a tower, and the wards were mostly four bedded bays which meant over time both my brother and I could get to know the other patients very well. It seemed that this block was mostly devoted to the care of older people and the ground floor taken up, as far as I could tell, by mental health patients who sometimes made their presence felt. Mum's ward on the second floor appeared to be full mostly of people who had suffered strokes. However, it soon became apparent on my first visit that most of the nursing staff, at least on this ward, were not used to dealing with patients who have dementia. I suppose there was no actual reason why they should have necessarily come into contact with such patients before but it did surprise me, and for a while caused me some concern.

On my brother's return from holiday my wife and I were also due to go on holiday to Rome for a week leaving on 7 July. In view of what was happening I did not want to go and made noises to that effect. In the end, however, I did go and am pleased I did so, even though Mum was never far away from my thoughts.

Mum's condition, after being admitted, remained more or less the same. She spent long periods with her eyes closed and her speech was incoherent. This made communication difficult particularly for the nurses. I had assumed, rightly as I was later to discover - that not opening her eyes was a symptom of the dementia. I tried to suggest this to some of the nurses and I think eventually, as her stay became extended, they realised this but certainly at the beginning some of them thought she was just very sleepy. It had been noticeable for a while that Mum would often fall to one side of the bed and that she had lost the ability to stay upright, even when half propped up, for any length of time. This meant that bed rails had to be in use all the time to ensure she did not fall out. Due to the difficulty in getting Mum to drink enough fluids and because at first it could not be established if she was able to swallow, she was put on a drip. Sometimes I would receive a surprise on visiting and her eyes would be open. She would appear to recognise me and would chat away incoherently and I would do my best to respond. On other occasions she would be lying to one side totally silent and not respond to my voice at all. I took her cassette tape player to the hospital on one occasion and played a tape of hymns. I thought this might stimulate some interest but although she had her eyes open and appeared to be listening there was no recognition of what she was hearing. I now think I was expecting too much.

Mum was taken by ambulance to Sutton Hospital for a brain scan. This appeared to show that Mum had suffered a stroke. The intention was for her to be seen by a speech and language therapist and also to receive some physiotherapy so that she could at least be moved out of bed into a chair. Unfortunately, the eventual decision was taken that she was not safe enough to sit in a chair and due to her lack of being able to communicate the speech therapy did not make any progress either.

The ultimate aim therefore was for us to find a nursing home for her as her condition was such that she could not return to Appleby. From mid July therefore we put all our efforts into searching for one which we felt would be right and I remained optimistic that once she had been discharged and was in a home which understood patients with dementia her condition would improve, if only slightly. We contacted Social Services at the hospital who later provided a list of homes. They also performed an assessment of Mum to determine her care needs which could then be sent to the nursing home we chose for their information and reference. When I was sent a copy of this assessment it had quite a profound effect on me. Up to that point nobody had given us much information before despite the fact that Mum had been in hospital for a month by that time. Now, reading about the extent of her care needs as a result of her very poor state of health made it somehow more definite and quite shocking.

It read like this:

"Mrs Spice has the following care needs:
- *24 hour nursing care and supervision;*
- *assistance with all areas of personal hygiene and daily living;*
- *full support to ensure she has a good diet and fluid intake;*
- *regular monitoring and changing of pads and regular offering the toilet;*
- *catheter care;*
- *pressure care and treatment for skin tears;*
- *assistance to change medication;*
- *emotional/psychological support for anxiety and confusion;*
- *hoisting for all transfers.*

Mrs Spice has a medical history of Ischaemic CVA and dementia and has recently experienced her first tonic/clonic seizure. She is confused and disorientated. She shows signs of anxiety when being turned and reluctance to comply with care at times. The ward has reported that she will grasp hold of the bed sheets or carer's arms/wrists when she is approached. She requires encouragement/persuasion to comply with care. Mrs Spice requires safety rails on her bed as she is unable to maintain her own safety. She requires two people to do a strip wash, toileting (day and night) and dressing.
She requires assistance from one person for grooming, mouth care and foot care and is unable to do any domestic tasks."

It really couldn't be any worse. Not having experienced a situation like this before I had an initial concern that her needs might be so great that there would not be a nursing home which could or would be prepared to take her. Of course those worries were unfounded as we did find a home in Woking which, although expensive, seemed perfect for her. At that time I was aware of NHS Continuing Care which means if a person's health needs are such that long-term nursing care is needed (as opposed to just social care) the NHS will pay. What I had not realised was that this free care is only awarded in relatively extreme cases. This has recently been well publicised in the media because it appears that people who have such care needs are being denied the funding to which they are legally entitled, and so are forced to sell their homes in order to be able to pay if they have no other means. In addition, case examples demonstrate that even if a patient's health needs mean they are eligible for funding, this might only be for a temporary period. Some of these cases include people with dementia where funding has been withdrawn when their condition is determined to have become "stable". The implication here seems to be that free NHS care will only be provided where the cause of the person's ill-health is short-term. For example, a person with dementia who may need everything to be done for them, has a fall and breaks a leg. In this case that person may well receive fully funded NHS care but as soon as they are assessed as being stable because the fracture has mended and recovery is considered to be complete, the funding can be taken away.

In other words, those individuals with illnesses that have a long-term cause are not being looked after as they are legally entitled to be – even though they are suffering from a terminal illness and will continue to need assistance at every level for the rest of their lives. The other issue is that those who can afford to pay because they have a property to sell are subsidising those who are being paid for by the State. As, in most cases, local authorities cannot afford the level of fees demanded by most nursing homes, those that are "self-funders" are being charged more as a result. This is yet another example of those who have savings through working hard all their lives are effectively penalised for having done so.

This issue is centred on financial resources which are, of course, limited, with the result that the concentration appears to be on how to make best use of the money, as opposed to giving priority to individuals' health needs on a case by case basis. How we would have fared with all of this had Mum lived we will now never know but it seems those who have been affected by such events have to be very persistent to get decisions reversed – some having to resort to court action to try to obtain a resolution. As it is believed that in years to come the number of older people in this country will increase, this whole situation is not a happy prospect for those of us who may eventually need nursing care ourselves.

We had visited four nursing homes in all, one being as far away as Godalming, since it became clear that not many had vacancies. Two of them I disliked personally because of the age of the buildings and the layout of rooms. Also one appeared to rely on bringing in care staff from overseas on a regular basis – something I didn't like the sound of from the point of view of continuity of care and staff getting to know the people they are caring for. I was also rather alarmed to discover just how far this home had to go to find care staff. It is a sign of the times that many poorly paid jobs are only attractive to foreign workers – be they immigrants or, as shown here, residents elsewhere, who have come into this country to work for limited periods at a time.

Another home in Cobham was excellent at first sight but there was something about the atmosphere and the way in which we were received that caused us to cross it off the list.

No matter how good the surroundings are, what matters more than anything else is the quality of care and attitude of the staff, particularly in Mum's case where she was not going to be in a position to appreciate the facilities or general environment of a particular home, but might have some awareness of the care she was receiving. I was keen to find a home in or around Woking, not only because visiting would be easier but because it didn't seem right that Mum was in hospital in Epsom and not, in say, St. Peter's at Chertsey, where my father had worked all those years and which was the hospital most local to Woking.

The nursing home in Woking we eventually chose fitted the bill exactly and they had vacancies. The home was split into two with one section being solely for EMI (elderly mentally ill) patients. The rooms were large and airy with wide corridors and the lounge and dining areas were inviting. All homes are inspected and as another part of the choosing process we had read the inspection reports on all the homes produced by the Commission for Social Care Inspection. None was perfect but the report on this one was better than most. Once the home had received a copy of Mum's community care assessment and confirmed they would take Mum, I was of course keen to put arrangements in hand for her to be transferred as soon as possible. God however had other plans.

During July Mum contracted MRSA. MRSA, which has been well publicised by the media, is a bacterium often found in 20 – 30% of the noses of normal healthy people and is also commonly found on people's skin. Most strains are sensitive to many antibiotics and infections can be effectively treated.

MRSA does not present a danger to the general public; it is usually confined to hospitals and in particular to vulnerable or debilitated patients like Mum. It is when the presence of this bacterium causes fever or inflammation that patients are considered to be infected and this can happen particularly following an operation or where the patient has a bladder catheter or surgical drain. These patients may also develop wound and skin infections and urinary tract infections as well. Perhaps this explained why the two skin tears on Mum's upper arm which had become infected were taking so long to heal. These were the wounds caused at the time of Mum's seizure at the end of June. The treatment for this illness is special antibiotics applied inside the nose as well as washing, bathing and hair washing with disinfectants. Scrupulous hand washing by hospital staff before and after contact with patients is the single most important infection control measure. This of course is to prevent the spread of MRSA from one patient to another. The other control measure is to isolate the patient who is infected by moving them into a single room with the door remaining closed. This is good provided a single room is available. I know in Mum's case there was a delay in her being moved because there were no one-bedded rooms vacant on her ward. I therefore can only guess at the effect of this delay on the other patients in her bay. I can also only guess at how Mum was feeling as a result of having this illness and it must have been the same for the staff. She did not appear to be unduly suffering but because she could not communicate we really had no idea other than the fact that she had a high temperature. When she was moved to a side room Mum was not affected at all because of her lack of awareness.

In fact the infection affected us more than her. On visiting I felt the isolation much more than Mum. There was nothing and nobody to look at or speak to. The room was quite small and the walls were completely bare and in need of redecoration. Quite frankly it was ghastly. We tried to cheer it up with vases of flowers and this helped a bit. Mum would occasionally have her eyes open when we visited and we would point the flowers out to her but it seemed that she could not really focus that well and any comment made was incoherent. I think Mum spent about two weeks in this room and eventually I came to prefer it. Had I known what was to happen in the not too distant future I would have wished Mum could have stayed there.

On one occasion when I visited Mum seemed quite alert. Her eyes were open and she was unusually responsive. What happened next was quite overwhelming causing me to have mixed feelings of happiness and sadness. On seeing me she made an "ahhh" sound and held one arm up to embrace me which she did. This moment did not last long but it was completely unexpected and took me right back to days gone by before this dreadful illness came between us.

This infection obviously delayed the possibility of Mum being discharged. She was eventually moved back to a different four bedded bay within the same ward at the end of July. However, this had no sooner happened than we were told Mum had a urinary infection which had to be treated. Presumably this was from having contracted MRSA, but, whatever the cause, she could not leave until this had been cleared up. Quite rightly, the hospital would not discharge her into the care of a nursing home in this condition but it was, nevertheless, a very frustrating time.

It seemed to be one thing after another and all I wanted was to get her out of hospital and into a nursing home which understood dementia patients and where I hoped she would improve. My brother, on the other hand, said on more than one occasion during this period that perhaps she would never leave. I don't know what made him think this apart from the fact that time was dragging on, but such a thought never entered my head and although he said it at least twice I immediately dismissed it. At that time there was nothing to suggest that these delays were more than hiccups which could and would be overcome.

It took longer than I expected for the urinary infection to be eradicated but on Thursday 11 August the drip containing antibiotics had been removed and I was told it had now been effectively treated. Things were looking up and there was at last talk of Mum being discharged. The nursing home in Woking was ready to receive her and I visited them to discuss dates for her admission which of course then had to be communicated to the hospital. We agreed a date of the following Monday 15 August. I arrived at the hospital at lunchtime that Thursday to feed Mum, as I had been doing regularly every other day for a number of weeks. I was fortunate in that I could easily visit at lunchtime which helped relieve the nurses from doing this task even if it was only once every other day. It was not an easy job and a great deal of patience was required. I often wondered how the nurses managed this task when they were always so busy. I imagined that it was very unlikely they would spend as much time as I did coaxing her to eat. Mum was unable to eat anything which required a lot of chewing but equally some items of food did take her a while to swallow nonetheless. On many occasions, however, depending on what food it was, just getting her to open her mouth was a feat in itself.

Although she would have her eyes closed for much of the time she seemed to always understand when it was meal times and putting a spoon to her mouth was enough for her to start taking food provided of course she liked the taste of it. It was interesting that despite Mum having lost her faculties to a great extent, she still had not lost the basic human ability to eat, even if a two course meal would sometimes take her forty minutes.

My one lasting memory of feeding her was the readiness of her accepting anything sweet. Whereas she often had to be endlessly encouraged to eat items of the main course, when it came to the pudding, her mouth often opened for the next mouthful before I was ready.

So on that Thursday I was more than usually optimistic that progress was at last being made. All arrangements were in place and we were looking for Mum to be discharged on the following Monday.

This optimism however turned out to be short-lived. After lunch a senior nurse arrived to tell me that Mum had developed another problem. She lifted the bedclothes from the lower half of the bed and showed me Mum's legs, one of which was very pale, almost white. Essentially Mum had developed a clot and as a result there was no blood circulating in the lower half of that leg, hence the very pale colour. A doctor then appeared which was unusual, taking into account the time of day. Managing to see the doctors on their normal daily rounds had not been easy, mainly because you never knew exactly what time they would arrive but I had been successful on a couple of occasions and I had also rung to speak to them during the MRSA period. On this occasion there was a serious reason for him turning up although at the time I did not appreciate this.

He confirmed the latest situation and said that they were going to administer drugs to try to disperse the clot, but were not sure if it would work. The other option was to operate but I was given the impression that in view of Mum's overall state of health, this was a non-starter. I couldn't believe what

I was hearing. It seemed I was being thwarted at every turn to get Mum out of that place.

On Friday 12 August I had not planned to go to the hospital but to visit the following day. However, at 5 pm I received a telephone call from the same hospital doctor. He started by asking if I was coming to the hospital and when I said not until the next day he said he had some news and was I happy to talk about it over the telephone. Still completely unsuspecting what he was about to say I agreed it was not a problem. He told me that the drug was not working and that the other option of surgery was not possible because they did not think she was strong enough to survive it. He then used the following words: "So we will make her comfortable". It may seem strange, and it certainly does to me now, but although I thought I knew what he was saying I wanted it spelt out because after everything that had happened, I couldn't quite believe that I understood correctly. What these words meant, of course, was that there was nothing more they could do for Mum except control any pain which she would experience as a result of the clot. He could not tell me how long she had to live but it would be weeks rather than months. It just did not seem possible that after all this time there would now be no discharge, no nursing home and finally no Mum. Even though it had been our plan for Mum to return to Woking, it appeared it was not to be and this we had to accept. However, despite this shocking news, I was not going to give in quite that easily. I now wanted Mum to be out of that hospital and back in Woking more than ever.

On my way home that very evening I visited Woking Hospice. As Mum had been a Woking resident for so many years I foolishly thought that having her transferred to this Hospice should not be a problem. In fact this was the case but sadly they did not have any vacancies.

I was to learn later from the palliative care team at the hospital that there was another hospice at Leatherhead, and that although they were at that point also full, this situation changed on a daily basis. At my request they agreed to check with both hospices every day and would let me know.

At first Mum's condition continued as before. She was still eating and drinking even if her eyes were shut but we were used to that by now. I was still visiting her but now increased it to every day. Other than feeding her there was not much to do so I would take some work with me, which I was able to do when I felt the ability to concentrate.

During the week of 15 August, however, her appetite decreased, and she developed a cough which necessitated the use of oxygen to help her breathe more easily. It was thought she had developed a lung infection which perhaps was not surprising having been confined to bed for so long. If only we could have got her to a nursing home much sooner maybe they would have managed to get her moving at least a bit; if only…

They had started to give Mum morphine for the pain which I realised she would have been experiencing, but of course she was unable to communicate the extent of it. I found this part the hardest of all; the fact that she could not say how she was feeling, how much pain she was in. On one occasion she seemed very unsettled and restless which I took to mean that she was in pain. I told the Sister who agreed to increase the morphine level, so I believe I was right, but how did they really know whether they were getting the dosage correct? How did they know they were giving enough medication to relieve the symptoms, and not too much which might precipitate coma or even death? They could only rely on their knowledge and experience and the reactions Mum displayed.

There has been a great deal of debate this year, 2006, about doctors who practise euthanasia, either voluntary or involuntary, who are popularly said to be "alleviating suffering". There was a study by a professor at Brunel University which appeared to indicate that 180,000 patients a year die after doctors withdraw or withhold further active treatment. There is also a suggestion that the end is hastened to relieve the pain and stress of the observer rather than the sufferer and that therefore the term "alleviating suffering" is just an excuse. In our case it is true that this period up to Mum passing away was difficult, but in fact could have been worse if Mum had been "compos mentis". The fact that she wasn't, and hadn't been for a while, did make the situation easier to bear from that point of view. We trusted the doctors when they said that they could not treat Mum further due to her weak and vulnerable state and of course they had attempted to use drugs to disperse the blood clot. But were they playing God with Mum's life?

Did they consider that because she effectively had no quality of life that this meant for all concerned it would be best to withdraw treatment and allow her to slip away with the assistance of morphine? During 2005 the Mental Incapacity Act gave legal force to "living wills" in which people can instruct doctors to withdraw treatment should they become too ill to make a decision.

I wonder how things would have been if Mum had made a "living will". Would this have made a difference in the situation we found ourselves in? We would still have had to trust the doctors that further treatment was not advisable, so would a "living will" have made things easier because we would have known that withdrawing treatment under these circumstances would have been what Mum wanted? The answer seems to be that in fact it would have made no difference, at least to us, the family, other than knowing that whatever actions the doctors decided to take were what Mum wanted to happen. A family would have no more input with regard to the outcome than we did ourselves without a 'living will', and I believe that this is as it should be.

It was a great sadness that while this was all happening to Mum, my brother's marriage broke down. Things had not been good for some time and it transpired that Mum's illness was the straw that broke the camel's back. The timing for him could not have been worse. I'm not sure what Mum would have said had she found out, but knowing her she would have been very supportive, and also maintained communication with both her son and daughter-in-law. That was Mum.

Food and drink eventually became impossible for Mum to take by mouth so a drip was inserted instead to feed her intravenously and keep her hydrated. It was during that week that another unreal incident happened. It came totally unexpectedly and only lasted for a moment – then it was over. Mum had to be turned every four hours and as the community care assessment confirmed, it was something she resisted, probably because she did not understand what they were doing. On this particular occasion I stayed while they did this. Suddenly Mum opened her eyes and looked straight at me and gave me this look. It was a look I knew from way back – she would give it if something amused her but she didn't want others to know her reaction because it would have been inappropriate. So it was a "secret look" that only those who knew Mum well would recognise and understand. On this occasion the "look" said several things to me all at once. "What are they doing now?" "Isn't this a wheeze – they think I'm ill but I'm only pretending really." "I've been lying here with my eyes closed but it's only a game I'm playing." This look had no sooner happened than it was gone, the eyes were closed once more, and things were back to "normal". I couldn't believe I had been there at the right time and in the right place to witness that "look" and I was absolutely delighted I had seen what I would later call one of Mum's lucid moments. Whether that's what it was or whether it was just a normal momentary reaction to what was going on around her that made this happen I don't know. It might have happened before and there had been nobody who would have seen and recognised it. Whatever the cause of that lucid moment I was so grateful to have witnessed it. I was well aware that it was most unlikely I would ever see it again.

Our families visited on Saturday 19 August and we hoped Mum knew they were there. She did not open her eyes once but she did a lot of mumbling in response to our talking to her so perhaps our words did get through. None of us knew that it would be the last time we would all be together, and certainly nothing was said between us to suggest this, but I thought more than once that it could be the case, and indeed it was.

On Monday 22 August, when I arrived at the hospital, I had a shock. The equipment that surrounded Mum's bed had been removed. I had had no warning of this and not surprisingly I immediately assumed this meant that the end was imminent.

The supply of oxygen had gone but this was not crucial anyway. It was more the fact that the drip had been taken away. This was devastating because it effectively meant that food and drink had been withdrawn. If the end was near nobody was saying this in so many words. I now regret not asking more questions about what was happening. At the time, however, I knew her passing was inevitable, and that in fact it was probably for the best despite my past optimism. She had no quality of life and there was nothing to suggest that this would have improved even if she had moved into a nursing home. Taking this all into account - wasn't withdrawing food and water in Mum's best interests? Under these circumstances I think most people would agree with me. However, I still felt that we should have been consulted before the action of withdrawing the drip was taken.

I still wanted Mum moved to a hospice, any hospice if there was space, but on that Monday this was still not possible. Although there were only three other people in Mum's bay, it was still too public in these circumstances, and I also worried about the effect on the other three patients of having someone terminally ill in their midst when they were all trying to get better. The lady next to Mum also had early stage dementia and was recovering from a stroke. Luckily she was not fully aware of what was going on around her. Diagonally, across from Mum was a lady in her 50s who had developed an ulcer-like place on her leg which had had to be lanced. She was in the ward longer than expected because it was taking time to heal due to complications after the operation. Mobility for her was a problem and she needed some physiotherapy. She was quite emotionally fragile and being in a ward with three elderly ladies was not helping her mental state.

Last but not least the fourth patient was a "Lady" and quite a character. Lady Dorothy Auckland had suffered a heart problem some weeks previously and been taken to St Thomas's Hospital for surgery. Her admission to Epsom was for her to continue to recover and to receive physiotherapy. She was a strong personality, very well spoken and called a spade a spade! If she did not like something you knew about it. However at the same time she was very caring and during the last two weeks of Mum's life was a great help to both Howard and me by being encouraging, supportive and thoughtful. Her presence in the ward also provided some comfort in that when we were not around she would keep a watchful eye on Mum and alert staff when she thought Mum was in need of their attention, as she did for the others when necessary. The staff soon found that Lady Dorothy was difficult to ignore. I was in the ward on the day she arrived and in fact I heard her before I saw her. The very first time our paths crossed was out in the corridor. Mum was being attended to and I was waiting to go back in. Lady Dorothy was walking with the aid of two sticks on her way to the bathroom with a nurse guiding her. I moved to one side thinking she would pass behind me but I had miscalculated. She appeared to be coming straight ahead towards me so naturally I moved again in order to get out of the way, at which point this loud booming voice said "Now which way are you going. I'm going over there" and pointed diagonally across towards a door on the right. I meekly apologised and moved again this time in the right direction, now I knew where she was headed. At the time I remember thinking "we've got a right one here" and so we had, but not for the reasons I had originally thought. She was a diamond and so touched was I by the support she had offered despite her own ailments that I returned to visit her after Mum passed away, to thank her for all she had done.

My efforts to move Mum into a hospice came to nothing in the end. Woking Hospice remained full and so was Leatherhead Hospice. Princess Alice Hospice in Esher was closed due to building works, which perhaps was one of the reasons for the lack of availability.

Finally, however on Tuesday 23 August, Leatherhead Hospice came up with the offer of a bed but I was to be thwarted again, this time by the palliative care team at the hospital. They decided that moving Mum at that stage would not be in her best interests and could be too uncomfortable for her. As I so wanted Mum to have the privacy I believed everyone deserves at a time like this, I was unhappy about the reason they gave for not moving Mum so I actually asked if it was because the end was near that it was considered a waste of time making the transfer. I was assured this was not the case but I could not help wondering all the same. Whatever the reason my hands were tied. There was nothing I could do.

That day Howard and I stayed at the hospital until 10.00 p.m. Nobody told us in so many words that there was little time left but I think we instinctively knew what was happening without having to be told, or even having to communicate the situation between ourselves. It was obvious, also as food and water had been withdrawn but we had no idea at the time how long Mum would stay with us. Due to this we could not decide what to do for the best. We could stay at the hospital overnight just in case or go and return first thing in the morning. Howard decided to do just that, said his goodbyes and left. I hung around for a while longer but eventually, albeit reluctantly, did the same.

The following day, Wednesday 24 August, we arrived at the hospital at 9 a.m. I had expected a phone call during the night from the hospital but it hadn't come so it seemed it was going to be another long day. On our arrival we found Mum's condition had not changed. She was, to all intents and purposes, unconscious but we tried talking to her in the hope she could hear. Neither of us found this very easy but we did our best. One thing we noticed on arriving was that the curtains were pulled around the bed. I did not think too much about this at the time, but now, looking back, I wondered if the nurses knew that the time was drawing near.

Coincidentally, the other patients had the curtains pulled round their beds as well. I assumed that this was because it was still early and they were being attended to and maybe that's all it was. I was very pleased to see the youngest of the patients, the one with the ulcerated leg, had been discharged. She had left just a couple of days ago and I was relieved that she was spared what was to happen.

At 9.30 a.m. with the whole day ahead of us I decided I could do with a shot of caffeine so we left the ward and went to the café in the main block. We were gone for around 30 minutes. On returning to Mum's bedside we were told that we had just missed the palliative care doctor and asked if we would like to see her. I never said no to a question like this. During the whole period Mum was in hospital I had had difficulty in obtaining information on Mum's condition. This was not all the hospital's fault. It was partly because I could not be on the ward at the time the doctors did their rounds although I tried to be as flexible as I could. There were a couple of times I actually telephoned the consultant for information but I found this less effective than seeing him face-to-face, particularly as English was not his first language. The palliative care doctor arrived within a few minutes. I asked if she could tell us how long Mum had to live and she said "Not long". How long was "not long" would have been my next question but just at that point Mum made a noise. I looked round at her to see her eyes very slightly open. She was resting slightly on her side facing towards me and I was holding her hand.

I noticed her breathing had become shallower and less frequent. At this point the doctor said she thought something was happening and was this what we wanted. This question could easily have been misconstrued. No, this whole situation was not what we wanted. She was only 77 years of age, a mere youngster. She should still be enjoying life, singing in the church choir, playing the piano, seeing her grand-daughters, Rachel and Nicola make their way in the world and her grandson, Jeremy go to university, driving her old Nissan Micra, living in her own house. Instead she's lying in a hospital bed with no quality of life whatsoever. *This wasn't how it was meant to be.* We had spent weeks planning for the future for her, all to no avail. No, this was definitely not what we wanted.

Of course, what the doctor was actually asking was whether we wanted to stay with Mum and there was no question that we would want to be anywhere else. Mum had waited until we returned from the café to leave – we certainly were not going from her side now. The three of us were left together. Howard on one side of the bed and me on the other, still holding Mum's hand and within a few minutes she was gone.

David told me later that what Mum did in waiting for us to return was a wonderful gift. Apparently most mothers wait until the family have gone before passing away and he, being a priest, should know. For some reason Mum wanted us to be there and whilst it was incredibly sad and distressing, it was something we will never forget and shall always be thankful to her and to God that we were so blessed in this way.

The following day we were extremely touched to receive a letter from Lady Dorothy which read as follows:

"Dear Robin and Howard,
It was a very sad moment for us all when your mother ascended into God's safe keeping; during the weeks I have been here the care, kindness, attention and gentleness the nurses gave her was impressive. I am sure this helped you

both in knowing that her welfare was paramount in their thoughts and time. May I praise you both for being such wonderful devoted sons and also thank you for the time you talked to me which helped me enormously to overcome the loneliness of a new ward. May I wish you and your respective families peace in the busy weeks ahead and secure in the knowledge that your mother is safely in God's keeping.

With all good wishes. Dorothy Auckland."

THE AFTERMATH

Summer 2005

The days immediately following did not allow much time for reflection. We were lucky to be able to register Mum's passing immediately whilst still at the hospital which saved us from having to return to do this on another occasion.

We had to wait of course for the death certificate to be issued by the doctor. She eventually arrived at the registrar's office and I recognised her as being one of the two doctors I had met previously on the ward on a few occasions in the last two weeks. When this doctor came to leave the office she looked in my direction and for some reason I smiled at her. The smile was not returned. Instead what I saw was someone who appeared to be somewhat embarrassed and uncomfortable at catching my eye. Admittedly she was only young, possibly mid 20s, so perhaps she did not have much experience of dealing with relatives of persons who had just passed away. But it wasn't as if we were intending to speak to each other, we weren't near enough to be able to do that. This then started me wondering why she had not felt able to smile or give some other look of reassurance. Perhaps I am reading too much into it but at the time and since I have wondered if there was something we did not know about Mum's death. We had been very compliant during the days prior to her passing. We had not particularly questioned anything or complained. I was upset that the drip had been removed and that we had not been given any warning or even been asked if this was acceptable to us but I did not say anything. I accepted and trusted that the doctors were the experts and knew what they were doing. Under the circumstances I cannot think we would have changed the decision made by the hospital but we would have welcomed being consulted, or even just told that this was the hospital's intention, rather than my turning up to find out without warning. So was this the reason for this doctor's apparent reluctance to smile. Perhaps she thought it inappropriate to smile back? Or was there some other reason? In the months since Mum passed away I have thought a great deal about what happened in the hospital during those interminable weeks. In particular, Mum contracting *Methicillin-resistant* S*taphylococcus Aureus* (MRSA). This is a purely hospital acquired infection which in Mum's case meant, apart from anything else, that she was lying stricken in a hospital bed for much longer than otherwise might have been the case.

I therefore cannot help wondering if these circumstances may have had something to do with the final outcome? Mum's death certificate states the causes of death as being *1(a) Septicaemia (b) Peripheral Vascular Disease.* Septiceamia is the presence of disease causing bacteria in the blood.

The human body has a range of different bacteria that live harmlessly in various places such as the mouth, skin and bowel but these bacteria can cause disease if they get into the bloodstream, particularly if a person is unwell or if their immune system isn't strong enough to keep the invading organisms under control. Other terms for septicaemia include bacteraemia and blood poisoning which I have since discovered can develop as a result of MRSA. I had previously thought that Mum had developed a blood clot in her leg due to the apparent propensity for her blood to clot as shown by her previous small strokes in the brain. I had also assumed that the fact that she had been bed-ridden for so many weeks was also a factor, in the same way that air travellers can develop deep vein thrombosis from sitting in one position for many hours. So all this, coupled with the fact that Mum had no quality of life, meant that I overlooked the possibility that the presence of MRSA could have played a part in her demise.

So was this the reason for the strange response by the doctor? Could Mum's death have been prevented if more scrupulous cleaning regimes had existed? It would be ironic for this to be the case, taking into account my father's occupation as a Domestic Services Manager where he was in charge of all the portering and cleaning staff, firstly at St Peter's Hospital, Chertsey and then latterly for all the hospitals in north-west Surrey. What he would have said about the widespread existence of these "superbugs" within our hospitals today will remain unknown but nonetheless intriguing to have found out. The thought that his wife may have passed away as a consequence of such an infection is as much ironic as it is a tragedy and of course it is best that he will never know.

Looked at another way, it could be said that her passing away so quickly was a blessing in disguise as Mum was a shadow of her former self and had no awareness of what was going on around her. Relatives of loved ones who have died in situations different from my mother, however, will of course feel very differently, as was recently seen in the television documentary entitled "What killed my Dad?" In that case a gentleman entered hospital for a hip replacement operation only to subsequently succumb to MRSA or similar infection from which he passed away. In our case perhaps it is best we don't know the answers to these questions.

David and his family were on holiday and did not return until two days after Mum passed away. David was aware prior to the holiday of Mum's condition so it was not a tremendous shock for him on his return. We wanted him to conduct the funeral as he had done for our grandmother in 1987. He came over to discuss the arrangements and in liaison with the funeral directors and the church, where Mum had been in the choir for so many years, a date of Friday 2 September was agreed for the funeral to take place.

We then had to decide the best way of informing people. Ideally I wanted to obtain what I will call "death announcement" cards. However, I found that these don't really exist or at least not in the retail outlets I visited. There seems to be a gap in the market here although since then I have seen one so perhaps somebody has woken up to this fact.

Anyway, as a result of not finding what we wanted we decided to produce our own. This turned out in fact to be the preferable option as we could personalise them in a way which would otherwise not have been possible. It did take more time but it kept me occupied which was a good thing.

A number of family members and friends attended the funeral including some cousins from Kent and I was particularly pleased they were able to come. There were also ten members of the choir in attendance all of whom, of course, had known Mum very well.

They very kindly sang the hymn "God be in my head" as an anthem during the service. In addition to this the funeral consisted of three hymns, Psalm 23, a reading by me, the eulogy written and given by David, and prayers. I wanted to be able to do a reading at the service but was not sure whether I could or indeed what I would read if I did.

Mum, the great hoarder that she was, used to keep any items she found of interest in the newspapers in case they might be useful in the future. When I was looking through a pile of these cuttings one day before the funeral I found a poem which I remember Mum showing to me at the time she cut it out of the paper. Not only was it very appropriate taking account of the subject matter, it was also humorous which I thought would make it easier for me to read without becoming upset. The poem is as follows, together with the preamble I gave at the service:

"As many of you will know my mother was a member of the choir at this church. She joined in 1973 a few months after I joined. My brother Howard was already a member but left in 1975 when his voice broke. I left in 1981 but Mum continued until 2003 when her illness started to take hold.

So for around 30 years she sang in the choir, initially as a second soprano but later as an alto at a time when altos were a bit thin on the ground. She didn't find singing alto that easy. Like me sight reading was not her strong point but being able to play the piano meant she could at least practise at home before choir practice and the Sunday services, so concerned was she to get it right. Being a soprano and then an alto meant she knew only too well the difference in singing the tune and having to sing an underneath part so in 1998 when she saw an item in the daily newspaper about an organist who had written a poem about being an alto, it really struck a chord and I remember we had a good laugh about it at the time.

My mother was a great cutter-outer of articles in newspapers and quite by chance last week I came across the poem again, so I thought I would share it with you today. So this is for my mother, the altos here today and I guess altos everywhere. It's called the Alto's Lament.

101

~ A Son's Story ~

It's tough to be an alto when you're singing in the choir

The sopranos get the twiddly bits that people all admire

The basses boom like loud trombones, the tenors shout with glee,

But the alto part is on two notes (or if you're lucky, three).

And when we sing an anthem and we lift our hearts in praises

The men get all the juicy bits and telling little phrases.

Of course the trebles sing the tune - they always come off best;

The altos only get three notes and twenty two bars rest.

We practise very hard each week from hymn book and the Psalter,

But when the conductor looks at us our voices start to falter.

"Too high! Too low! Two fast!- you held that note too long!"

It doesn't matter what to do – it's certain to be wrong!

Oh! Shed a tear for altos, they're the Martyrs and they know,

In the ranks of choral singers they're considered very low.

They are so very 'umble that a lot of folks forget 'em;

How they'd love to be sopranos, but their vocal chords won't let 'em!

And when the final trumpet sounds and we are wafted higher,

Sopranos, basses, tenors – they'll be in the Heavenly Choir.

While they sing "Alleluia!" to celestial flats and sharps,

The altos will be occupied with polishing the harps.

The identity of the author of this poem is unknown as he only gave his name as "Bob the organist" and has never been published. What we do know is that a copy of this poem was found behind the vestry door of a church at Sutton Coldfield in the West Midlands and became a hit when it was featured in a poll run by the radio station Classic FM after being sent in by a listener. It subsequently topped Classic FM's poll to find the nation's 100 favourite humorous poems. Back in 1998 when this poem came top, all attempts to find "Bob" drew a blank so exactly who and where he is remained a mystery. There is no doubt that many people, including my mother thought it a brilliant piece of writing As it was so popular I can only think there must be an awful lot of altos out there!

The reading of the poem was followed shortly afterwards by the eulogy. This was not only an accurate précis of Mum's life but was uniquely given from the perspective of someone who, though more distantly related, was nevertheless a significant recipient of Mum's devotion to her family.

Epilogue

2006

Mum has now been gone for over 10 months at the time of writing. It is true what they say, time is a great healer but of course I can never forget and nor would I want to. There are all sorts of reminders of her past presence, some more upsetting than others. For me, the large number of photographs of her are a comfort whereas the wardrobe full of her clothes remained a no-go area for a long time. Places we used to visit regularly together are also reminders and remain a source of sadness. For me, it is the garden centre we would go to each week for lunch. For Howard, it is the supermarket where they used to shop.

Mum was always well-groomed and her clothes beautifully cared for even though some must have been over 20 years old when she passed away. Due to their age her favourites appear in photographs time and again and for this reason in particular it has been difficult to even look at them, never mind let them go. It was easy to dispose of most of the clothes she wore at Appleby. Not only did I not want a reminder of that period but they did not evoke the same feelings or happy memories.

A few weeks ago I took the plunge and opened the wardrobe doors because I decided the time had come for other people to have the benefit of wearing the clothes. That's what Mum would have wanted but it wasn't going to happen if they stayed where they were. I had to be strong. I started removing them from their hangers and folding them up, and I was okay. It seemed I had chosen the right time to do this task. I eventually reached a coat which we had bought together in around 2003. It was a blue (her favourite colour) three-quarter length lightweight coat for the spring and autumn which she came to wear quite a lot because it was comfortable. It was one of only two coats that went with her to Appleby and I had kept it really only because it was so new. I removed it from the hanger and before I folded it up decided to check the pockets. One was empty but the other contained something wrapped in a serviette. I unwrapped it – only to find a biscuit. A Rich Tea biscuit which she had hidden in her pocket some time during her stay at Appleby. I completely dissolved. Such a simple find seemed to symbolise for me in a powerful way the events of the last three years of her life.

Dementia is a truly horrendous illness to develop for both the person it afflicts and their families. The more people understand this illness and its effects the quicker help and advice can be provided to those who need it, as I hope our experience, as related here, has shown.

It is fair to say that although Mum only passed away in 2005, we effectively lost her much longer ago, such is the devastating nature of the illness. Our efforts to maintain normality were always destined to fail in the end but as her sons I believe we had a duty to help her in the best way we could for as long as we could despite, at times, the very trying circumstances. Just as she was always there for us so I wanted us to be there for her. I plead guilty to being naïve, if that's how it appears, to believing that we could make a difference to Mum's situation when it was probably obvious we were wasting our time and energy.

For a long time we tried to find the way, more or less, by ourselves because we had not realised we needed, or could have benefited from, expert advice. We knew of the existence of agencies that are qualified and able to help people in our position. But initially we did not tap into these resources when the advice was most needed – i.e. during the early stages of the illness. It is at the beginning, when family members are feeling worried and bewildered by what is happening, that professional advice is crucial. Without it, those who are trying to support the sufferer blunder along, making many mistakes along the way owing to their own failure to understand.

Although we acted with the best of intentions, for the majority of the time Mum did not appreciate our efforts and did not want any help because she failed to recognise <u>she</u> needed it. However, much of this denial and negativity was of course the illness, not her at all, and I tried to remember that when the going got tough. In the end, despite everything, the important thing was that we tried to be *there* for her, and I had no greater teacher of this than my mother herself, Julie Spice.

Printed in the United Kingdom
by Lightning Source UK Ltd.
130883UK00001B/152/A